Mechatronics Engineering

Other Handbooks of Interest from McGraw-Hill

Mechatronics Engineering

Donald Tomkinson

James Horne

McGraw-Hill

New York San Francisco Washington, D.C. Auckland Bogotá
Caracas Lisbon London Madrid Mexico City Milan
Montreal New Delhi San Juan Singapore
Sydney Tokyo Toronto

Library of Congress Cataloging-in-Publication Data

Tomkinson, Donald.
Mechatronics engineering / Donald Tomkinson, James Horne.
p. cm.
Includes bibliographical references and index.
ISBN 0-07-065099-3.
1. Mechatronics. I. Horne, James. II. Title.
TJ163.12.T66 1995
621—dc20 95-32909
CIP

McGraw-Hill 
A Division of The ***McGraw-Hill*** *Companies*

1 2 3 4 5 6 7 8 9 0 DOC/DOC 9 0 0 9 8 7 6 5

ISBN 0-07-065099-3

The sponsoring editor for this book was Robert Hauserman, the editing supervisor was Bernard Onken, and the production supervisor was Donald Schmidt. It was set in Century Schoolbook by Ron Painter of McGraw-Hill's Professional Book Group composition unit.

Printed and bound by R. R. Donnelley & Sons Company.

This book is printed on recycled, acid-free paper containing a minimum of 50% recycled de-inked fiber.

Dedicated to Pamela, Cathy,
Zachary, and Jessica.

Contents

Part

1

Definition of Need

Chapter

1

Introduction

1.1 Objective

The objective of this book is to formulate a disciplined methodology to develop products by ensuring interaction between mechanical, electrical, and software engineers. Typically the interaction between these functional areas has been tenuous at best. More often than not the interaction is serial in nature, rather than parallel and cooperative. It is important that mechanical, electrical, and software engineers consider all constraints of the product life cycle, including design, manufacturing, and service, as soon as possible in the development cycle.

The need to be responsive to customer requirements dictates that manufacturers have effective marketing, design, manufacturing, and service after the sale. Unfortunately, the disconnect between mechanical, electrical, and software engineers can cripple the process of getting products to market in an effective and efficient manner. The conflicts between the engineering groups are illustrated and a detailed methodology—mechatronics—is proposed to help resolve the conflict. The groups must work to be one cohesive team. Functional excellence does not ensure competitiveness; team excellence facilitated by a mechatronic approach does.

To help understand the conflict, the business drivers affecting most manufacturers today are discussed. Additionally, there are constraints which dictate the product design, manufacturing, and service. These drivers help facilitate the environment for an adversarial relationship between mechanical, electrical, and software engineers because of the conflicting nature of the pressures from both a global and product-related perspective. These drivers can affect each of the functional areas differently. How does an organization effectively address these business drivers? The drivers can be considered constraints by a manufacturer. However, the forward-looking company views the drivers as opportunities. To view the drivers as opportunities is a state of mind in some cases as well as a disciplined process to leverage the drivers. A disciplined process such as mechatronics provides some of the answer because it focuses on the total problem. The key is to consider all the drivers as simultaneously as possible. It is not optimal to consider how the drivers affect mechanical engineers first, then how they affect electrical engineers next, and so on. There is a significant chance that the functional area may be optimized while suboptimizing the whole when the effect of the business drivers is considered on each functional area separately.

The specific content of today's products and how that content drives each of the disciplines is detailed to help understand what drives the design, manufacturing, and service of the products. The product content discussed applies to most products purchased today including automobiles, jets, mechanical machinery, white goods, and consumer electronics. To facilitate the understanding, existing methods are contrasted with the mechatronic method.

The product development process that an organization uses (ad hoc or specifically defined) is generally highly influenced by the types of products which are being developed. This process provides the day-to-day interaction between electrical, mechanical, and software engineers. The current, somewhat ad hoc interaction is discussed and contrasted with the proposed mechatronic method. In some cases, a mechatronic approach has already been adapted by several forward-thinking companies in a full-scale or pilot implementation. Examples of the implementation of mechatronics are highlighted to show that mechatronics can be a reality, not just some theoretical discussion.

In the most important section of this book, the key items to achieve a mechatronic approach are detailed. This is where the rubber meets the road and determines if mechatronics is a theoretical or a practical method. Understanding how to implement mechatronics is important to all levels of the organization from top management to individual contributors. This discussion focuses on the organization structure required to achieve mechatronics, and the education and training needed to make mechatronics a reality.

Achieving a mechatronic approach is contingent upon not only the organization structure and education, but what tools are available. The tools can be manual tools, such as an organized process, or software-based tools. Both types of tools are important, and their role in making mechatronics a reality is detailed. Software-based tools require integration in order to significantly affect team results. As such, the infrastructure required is discussed.

Implementing a mechatronic approach is a well-defined process. It requires certain steps to define the existing process, identify the desired process, and execute a plan which achieves the desired process. Many times a phased implementation is the correct methodology. It is important to note, however, that implementing a mechatronic approach is somewhat dependent on the organization's culture and existing methodologies. The objective of this section is to provide guidelines to make mechatronics a reality because technology without implementation does not have much value.

A conclusion highlighting the key points to facilitate a mechatronic approach is reviewed for the purposes of reinforcing the concepts to help ensure that mechatronics is not a flash in the pan. The benefits of such a methodology are discussed to facilitate the acceptance of the value of a mechatronic approach.

Last, a supplier list including companies that offer mechatronic-related software solutions, design shops that specialize in mechatronic applications, analysis software companies, and database translation companies is provided. Additionally, a glossary of terms and a list of references is detailed along with a bibliography for further reading.

1.2 Overview

Today's manufacturer faces a plethora of obstacles to achieve success in the global marketplace. Customer requirements must be reviewed and prioritized and their feasibility must be assessed. Based on the priority and feasibility, the manufacturer can determine what is the best methodology to provide the functionality which will meet the requirements. This response is in the form of a product or products. The product content must be determined, and the form, fit, and functions are detailed. The manufacturer needs to decide how much new technology will be used and how much of the design and manufacturing will be performed internally vs. outsourcing some or all of these steps. All this and more must be considered in the attempt to be successful with a product introduction. Much has been written on these and other subjects, proposing what the manufacturer must do to maximize competitiveness. One thing is clear: success requires a disciplined approach utilizing a multifunctioned team. In the 1980s, quality and manufacturing excellence were keys to competitiveness, whereas a disciplined product development capability will be paramount as we enter the twenty-first century.[1] A mechatronic approach facilitates a disciplined process. A formalized, flexible process is required to meet and deal with most of the everyday situations. Management can then focus on managing exceptions. Today, in many cases, all situations are managed as exceptions. This is expensive and ineffective; it is also unnecessary.

Getting a design into production is never easy. In most cases, servicing a product after the sale is even more difficult. Inevitably there are glitches: Parts don't fit, or the parts cannot be easily assembled and disassembled or maybe something is left out entirely. Mechanical, electrical, software, and manufacturing engineers, often meeting for the first time, usually end up pointing fingers. After obligatory concessions and last-minute modifications, everyone returns to their work areas and the process is repeated until the product must be hastily released.

Engineers at one firm, for example, relate how they got out of a jam by cutting a hole in the side of an air-handling system to install a controller that someone overlooked. But as products become more complex, ad hoc revisions like this will not compensate for poor design and will not lead to acceptable results. They are suboptimum. Engineers of all types will have to work together to consider all the constraints over the product life cycle including performance, manufacturing cost, and serviceability costs. It sounds easy enough, but getting there is an uphill battle. Those companies who have a disciplined and well-defined product development process where electrical, mechanical, and software engineers work together closely will be the ones competing in the next century. Some companies—like Canon and Philips, because they already use a disciplined process—have the capability to bring products to market more quickly than competitors who have a purely ad hoc, creative process.[1]

A lot of manufacturers seem to be restructuring their workforce around specific markets and products. Each new operating group has its own purchasing, finance, engineering, production, marketing, and sales personnel. The idea is to improve time to market, quality, and ultimately competitiveness through closer cooperation of all personnel from identifying the customer need to developing a product to manufacturing and delivery of the product to support after the sale.

There is a similar push within engineering. In some firms, mechanical, electrical, software, packaging, and manufacturing engineering are coming together with one goal in mind—the product. The approach is called "mechatronics," and it is spawning a new breed of "intelligent" components and systems that combine an optimum blend of mechanics and electronics. A process which facilitates this interaction is long overdue.

In some respects, mechatronics is an extension of simultaneous engineering. However, the latter generally brings together only design and manufacturing. Mechanical, electrical, and software engineers continue to work apart, and each group deals with manufacturing and service individually. Although the approach is manageable with simpler products, it does not allow trade-offs across traditional design, manufacturing, and service boundaries. Nor is it effective for more complex products. Today's products are decidedly more complex than products introduced just 5 years ago. By definition and practice, a mechatronic approach requires trade-offs during development, thereby optimizating results based on a wide variety of criteria associated with product life cycle constraints.

Mechatronics is more than mere collaboration between mechanical, software, electrical, and manufacturing engineers. It goes beyond form, fit, and function. Mechatronics means applying mechanical and electrical design knowledge simultaneously, early in development considering life cycle constraints, usually in a computer-aided environment. It means making trade-offs between mechanical dynamics and accuracies and electronic intelligence. For example, a car designer may specify low-cost, low-tolerance solenoids if the inaccuracies are compensated by sensors, microcontrollers, and precision control algorithms. Such trade-offs can be optimized only in a mechatronic environment with engineers of many functions in constant communication. Additionally, a medium such as a digital mock-up facilitates the communication so that the communication is more than just mere words. "A picture is worth a thousand words" is absolutely applicable in this environment.

Regrettably, integration of electronics into a physical space has occurred more by coincidence than by design. In the early days of CAD, either electrical or mechanical design was automated to improve design capabilities. During the seventies and eighties, design and manufacturing professionals witnessed the evolution of design to manufacturing automation within either the electronics or mechanical environment. To describe how the design environment "talked" to the manufacturing environment, "integration" became the buzz word.

For manufacturers to address their problems, the solution must be more than a buzz word. Manufacturers need to ensure electrical and mechanical engineers are working in a collaborative environment considering design, manufacturing, and service constraints as early as possible to ensure effective and efficient product development. Handoffs and communication will be rapid and smooth to facilitate responsive and comprehensive product development. However, we cannot expect engineers who have rarely worked together to all of a sudden see the light and start working together in a collaborative manner. Training and education is required. It starts at the college level where electrical, mechanical, and software engineers are separated in the informative years where the engineering curriculum is starting to be applied. This needs to be corrected to include mechatronic curriculums so that mechatronics in the work environment can be a reality. A mechatronic approach will help achieve a systematic method which is necessary for companies to compete in today's global environment.

1.3 History of Mechatronics

Even though mechatronics-based products today are around us everywhere, the combination of electricity, mechanisms, and control in products is a relatively recent technology. It appears that we are in the midst of a continuing mechatronic revolution with the introduction of CD players or micromachines to be used in surgery. In fact we are really just stopped at a moment in time on an evolution that started over three hundred years ago. Interestingly, some of the great people of science have been involved in the evolution of mechatronics.

Early Greece. The word *ēlektron,* meaning amber, was used in early Greece to describe the static electricity induced when amber was rubbed with fur.

1642. Mechanical digital calculating machine invented by Blaise Pascal.

1769. James Watt invented the "flyball governor." The flyball governor was used as a feed-backward control mechanism to regulate steam flow, thereby maintaining a constant engine speed in a steam engine.

1801. Joseph Jacquard of France implemented the first example of feed-forward control by using punched cards to program the patterns woven by a loom. This invention allowed manufacturers to preprogram a weave into punched cards. This automatic control of a manufacturing process with its punched cards operating in a binary fashion was the precursor to modern numerical control.

1800s. First theoretical analysis of a control system developed for the Watt governor by Scottish physicist James Clerk Maxwell. The set of differential equations used to describe the behavior of the Watt governor is the beginning of the field of control theory.

1888. The alternating-current induction motor was invented by Nikola Tesla.

1908. Elmer Sperry patents a system for stabilizing large ships with gyroscopes. Later he went on to use gyroscopes to stabilize the flight of aircraft.

1924. The predecessor of IBM, Computing Tabulating Recording Company, is founded by Herman Hollerith.

1931. Michael Faraday discovers the law of induction, that a changing magnetic field can induce a changing current. This discovery was the basis of the electric motor and the electric dynamo.

1937. John Atanasoff starts work on the first electronic computer for resolving linear equations. By 1942 an operational version, called ABC, is working with punched card input.

1946. The first electronic digital computer was built at the University of Pennsylvania by J. Presper Eckert and John Mauchly.

1947. The transistor was invented at Bell Telephone Laboratories by John Bardeen, Walter Brattain, and William Shockley.

1952. The numerical controller was invented at MIT. The machine was built from over 2000 mechanical valves and occupied a very small room.

1962. Unimation builds the first industrial robot.

1967. The term "mechatronics" was coined by Yasakawa Electric America.[2] The term, documented in the corporate history of Yasakawa, shows an evolution in thinking at Yasakawa from purely mechanical systems to systems based on integrated mechanisms, electronics, and control.

1970s. Engineers develop the first "micromechanisms." These are mechanical components that are typically machined using processes of the semiconductor industry. The first practical use of this technology was for automotive pressure sensors where a high-precision diaphragm is fabricated directly on the silicon of the sensing circuit.

1971. First microprocessor developed by Intel Corporation. The Intel 4004, "the world's first 'computer on a chip'."[3]

1972. Fanuc launches a redesign of the numerical controller. The design team attempts to replace all mechanical components with electronic components because of the relative cheapness, compactness, and reliability of the electronics. Offshoot technology became the stepping motor.

1971 and 1978. Japanese Ministry of International Trade and Industry (MITI) passes legislation that encouraged joint research between the machinery and electronics industries.

1973. Computervision launches the first commercial CAD/CAM system.

1990. *Mechatronics* journal launched in the U.K. by Pergamon Press. This journal covers technical innovations in the field of mechatronics.

How industry got to this point in history is only part of the mechatronics story. Later this book discusses in much greater detail the pressures on manufacturers today that force them to take an even stronger look at mechatronics than they did 2, 5, or 10 years ago.

1.4 Definition of Mechatronics

The term "mechatronics" has not been used widely in the United States and has been used only recently in Europe. Most conferences on mechatronics still tend to have a portion of at least one session that discusses the definition of mechatronics. This book, instead of trying to create a new definition of mechatronics, will adopt the definition that has been widely used by the European Economic Community:

> Mechatronics is the synergistic combination of precision mechanical engineering, electronic control and systems thinking in the design of products and manufacturing processes.[4]

The word "fusion" has been used in some definitions in place of synergistic. Whereas mechanical engineering might be considered to be the synergistic combination of fluid dynamics, mechanics, thermal dynamics, and material science, to name a few, mechatronics is the synergistic combination of mechanical engineering, electronic control, and systems thinking.

The words "systems thinking" used in conjunction with mechanical engineering and electronic control are a very important aspect of this definition. The systems thinking approach allows a designer to weigh the alternatives between solutions presented from the mechanical, electrical, or control engineering arenas. It is this synergistic systems engineering approach that distinguishes mechatronics from concurrent engineering, mechanical engineering, and electrical engineering.

John Millbank of the University of Salford, U.K., summarized the system level approach in the following way:

> By definition, then, Mechatronics is not a subject, science or technology per se—it is instead to be regarded as a philosophy—a fundamental way of looking at and doing things, and by its very nature requires a unified approach to its delivery.[5]

The next section takes a specific look at the difference between mechatronics and some of the other trends of the time such as total quality management or concurrent engineering. This is done to clearly demonstrate that mechatronics is not just another trendy topic to consume a company's time but is an approach that has its own added value to a company's competitiveness.

1.5 Relationship to Other Fields and Topics

Is there value added in the application of mechatronics to the product design process? Why not stick strictly to some of the more popular and trendy product development practices such as Concurrent Engineering or Total Quality Management? After all, companies are having enough difficulty mastering one or more of these cultural changes. Do they really have room in the corporate culture to develop the concept of mechatronics?

This section examines three major strategic "bandwagons" that companies are currently climbing on board, concurrent engineering, ISO 9001, and TQM, then notes how mechatronics complements each of these bandwagons and in many ways can be used as an effective tool to implement the strategies themselves. This section also discusses some of the additional benefits that mechatronics brings to a company. These benefits and how a company can achieve them are highlighted throughout the rest of the book.

The term "bandwagon" is not used in a negative sense. It is used only to indicate how companies striving to be competitive on a worldwide basis lock on to a particular ideology, for example, that preached by TQM or necessary to gain ISO 9001 certification. In many instances tackling one of these cultural paradigms can cause such cultural change that the organization goes into cultural shock, preventing it from looking at other methodologies. Because mechatronics is very focused in its integration of two disciplines, it actually can be implemented at the same time any of the other paradigm shifts are applied.

1.5.1 Concurrent engineering

Concurrent engineering, or the notion of designing the product for minimized production costs, is actually not a new topic. As early as 1968, C. A. Gladman emphasized that products should be designed "right-first-time for production" so that manufacturing resources were used effectively. Further work has been done to study manufacturing cost reduction or design for manufacture. Boothroyd[6,7] has received special attention in the United States for his pioneering work in design for manufacture (DFM). In Europe the term "Design for Economic Manufacture" (DEM) is used the same way DFM is used in the United States. The term Simultaneous Engineering is also frequently used, but most people who practice it admit that it is just another term for Concurrent Engineering. Whether it is called Concurrent Engineering, DFM, DEM, or Simultaneous Engineering, there are two common themes.

The first is that the initial design work must account for the needs of all affected downstream processes. This theme further focuses on the timeliness of these considerations. People from a variety of disciplines are brought together as early in the design process as possible to determine the entire strategy and life cycle of a product. They might consider, for example, whether functional trade-offs could be made to shorten the product development cycle, which in turn could lead to greater market share.

The importance of timeliness of these decisions to concurrent engineering and to a company's general financial success is readily illustrated in Fig. 1.1. Note that 60 to 80 percent of the product costs have been committed by the time the design process is complete.

Typically a company's first efforts to consider downstream processes early in the design bring together the design and manufacturing departments. Instead of postponing manufacturing decisions, the new team makes them concurrently with product design decisions. Boothroyd revolutionized engineers' approach to considering the manufacturing implications of design by developing the concept of DFM and enabling it to be done simply with software tools and a database of cost information.

Another very important theme of concurrent engineering is "better

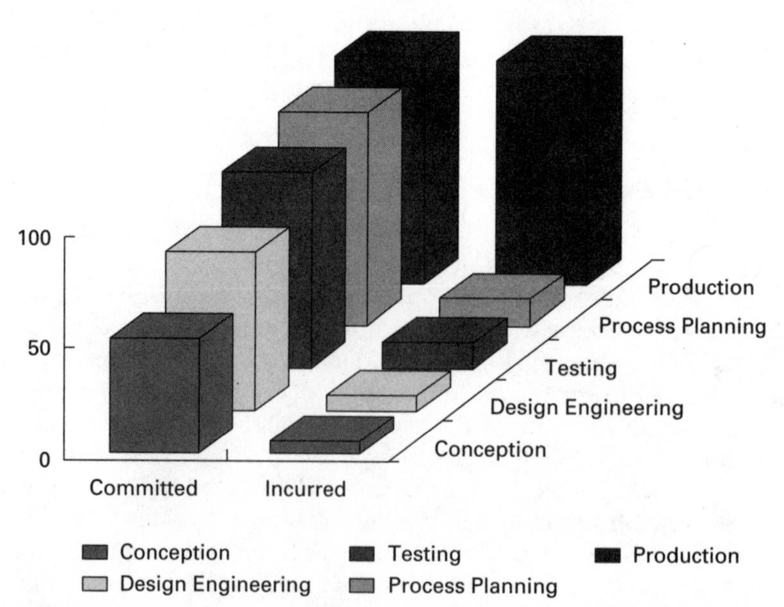

Figure 1.1 Product costs as a function of product life cycle. (*Computer-Aided Manufacturing-International, Inc.*)

teamwork."[8] It is all very well for a company to force two or more organizations to work together, but realistically they won't cooperate until there is teamwork at all levels. This usually happens as the various organizations realize that it is in their interest to do so. In today's company the biggest incentive for teamwork is that a competing company has mastered teamwork as a critical step in concurrent engineering. To effectively implement CE, everyone brought together should be instilled with "the idea that people can do a better job if they cooperate to achieve a common goal"[8].

Implementations of Concurrent Engineering usually take one of two forms, largely because it is, for most highly departmentalized companies, a monumental undertaking. The first approach is to spin off a smaller organization outside the mainstream of standard corporate bureaucracy and force it to implement CE. This concept was used very successfully by Chrysler Motors for the design of the Viper car.

The second approach is to implement CE within the standard corporate structure. One common way to do this is to start integrating the activities of two departments, add a third department, and so forth until all departments are working cooperatively using the CE model.

1.5.2 Total Quality Management

Total quality management has at its roots the work pioneered by E. Deming in the United States in the early 1950s at MIT. He later took his concepts to Japan, where they were readily adopted in the reconstruction of Japan. Subsequently Europe and the United States started to focus attention on Total Quality Management (TQM) as they felt their market share and quality leadership dwindle against stiff Japanese competition. Deming's philosophy of total quality management is distilled into 14 principles that define a process of continuing improvement. This overall quality improvement process (see Fig. 1.2) starts with a definition of the current process and builds an improved process in iterative cycles. (Identification of the current process is also at the heart of the ISO 9001 certification process.) In the initial definition phase only 80 percent of the department may be using the same procedures. Once the current process has been defined, it can be modified for improvement and implemented consistently. As new people come on board they must also be trained in the new procedures.

Even though the process of continuous improvement may appear to be focused on itself, in reality each step is taken only if there is an im-

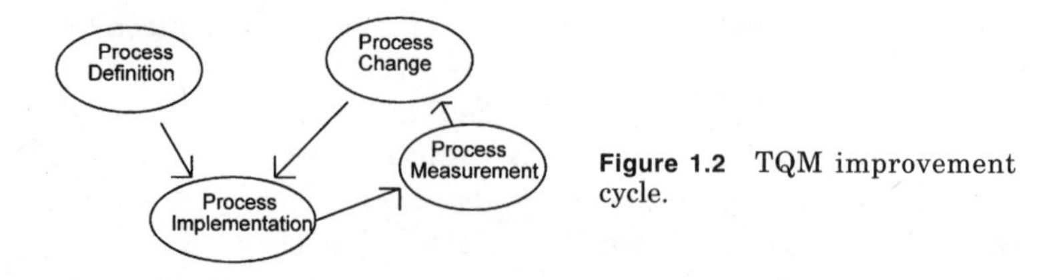

Figure 1.2 TQM improvement cycle.

provement as perceived by the customer. The customer is the major focus of this activity.

Once the procedures of the department are well defined and everyone has started using them, they can be measured to determine how effective they really are. These measurements should be based on how well the current procedures satisfy the end customer.

With a clear measurement of how current procedures support the company's goal of satisfying its customers, the company can start to define a new set of procedures that will better satisfy the customer. This new set of procedures, or process change, must in turn be implemented prior to trying to improve it again.

Clearly the procedures that the mechanical and electronics engineers use to interact and communicate could be subjected to this type of TQM scrutiny. For example, the engineers could agree that their joint designs would be simulated with a simulation package such as Saber to determine the sensitivity of the various system components to variances in tolerances. The output of this could be fed back into the design process as an instructive illustration of how changes in an environmental variable such as temperature can affect both the mechanism and the electronics. The outcome should be continuously improving interaction between mechanical and electronic engineers, allowing them to better satisfy their customers.

1.5.3 ISO 9000

ISO 9000 is a standard used by many businesses within the European Economic Community (EEC) to assure a minimum level of focus on the TQM process in areas such as marketing, sales, services, engineering, and manufacturing. More and more suppliers to major companies in the EEC must have ISO 9000 certification in order to do business in Europe. To become certified, a company or division must be able to demonstrate that they are at the start of the TQM improvement cycle; that is, they have defined their processes.

In most companies ISO 9000 certification is introduced as a marketing and competitive strategy to address more and more "requests for proposal" from Europe. These requests require documentation on what steps the company is taking to become ISO 9000 certified.

Becoming ISO 9000 certified is not a trivial process. Most companies spend a great deal of time, energy, and money to get there. To meet the goal, companies send people to training courses, spend money on independent audits to determine if they are ISO 9001 compliant, and consume hours of staff time documenting the company's procedures and processes.

Large companies typically become ISO 9000 certified one division or department at a time. Most divisions find that their own certification is a large enough issue, never mind the challenges of coordinating the certification process across divisional boundaries. If the division includes engineering disciplines, the evaluation must include both the mechanical and electronics departments and their interactions. Through the process of self-examination forced by ISO 9000, the initial cooperation between the mechanical and electronics engineers can take seed.

1.5.4 How does mechatronics fit into one of these corporate strategies?

What is competing for the time of management and the resources of the company should now be clear. On one hand there is pressure to design better products. A company can easily lock onto a global solution to this problem in the form of concurrent engineering. Then there is the pressure to do business in Europe, which typically requires a company to consider ISO 9000 certification. Finally, owing to the push for quality from Asia, many companies also strive to use the concepts of TQM. With all these forces pulling at a company, will it have time for mechatronics, and is there any benefit in doing so?

The answer is clearly yes. Mechatronics is complementary to these other strategies. The fundamental concept of mechatronics, bringing together mechanical and electronic disciplines, is best implemented on a local scale. Implementing one of these other strategies at a corporate level better allows mechatronics to be used as a straightforward problem-solving strategy at the grass-roots level. Once the mechanical and electronic disciplines are brought together, they can achieve mechatronics within the framework of the other corporatewide strategy (see Fig. 1.3).

Certainly the two departments working together will perform their share of interdepartmental coordination and start to fulfill the CE model. Naturally these two departments will also need to cooperate with other departments to fulfill the corporatewide CE model. Inter-

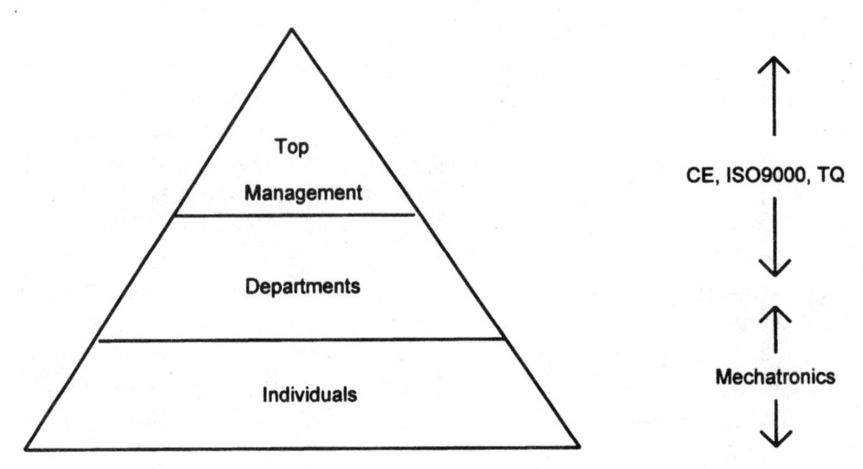

Figure 1.3 Integration of mechatronics with corporate strategies.

acting mechanical and electronics departments can also document and iteratively improve their process, which both satisfies the major thrust of ISO 9000 and gets to the heart of TQM.

1.5.5 Why start with mechatronics?

Once mechanical and electronic engineers are brought together under the auspices of, for example, CE, how do they actually build a product better with combined technologies? Exactly how do they move away from current practices? This book provides this guidance. Mechatronics, whether defined in this book or studied in journals and papers, provides engineers with specific, detailed information about how to integrate two departments and how to better design products and production processes through the integration of these disciplines.

All the corporate strategies discussed could be applied to the design of any product or to organizations with focuses other than product design. Because they are so general, they tend not to make tangible recommendations. For example, a common recommendation of total quality management is to make processes repeatable. This type of recommendation, though it is very valuable and potentially has a great return on investment, is overwhelming to implement compared to a specific recommendation to use photosensors to track product position in a continuous manufacturing line instead of discrete work cells with mechanical stops. This recommendation to trade off between electronic and mechanical disciplines is not only mechatronics in action but is tangible enough to implement easily.

Another reason to start with mechatronics is that it is a smaller, more manageable project. From a corporate point of view concurrent engineering is an excellent idea. From an implementation point of view it can be a nightmare unless taken in small doses. In a large company with major vertical organizations, or "chimneys,"[9] it will be far easier to break down the barriers between two chimneys than to merge all the chimneys at once. Don Clausing recommends that implementation of a fundamental cultural change such as concurrent engineering should start in a "core group." This core group actually adopts concurrent engineering, or in this case concurrent mechanical-electronic engineering. With a successful pilot in place, top management can be educated on the benefits of the cooperation between these two departments before extending the concept to other groups.

1.5.6 Mechatronics added value

Let's look at the reason for tackling mechatronics at all. CE, TQM, and ISO 9000 all offer motives to be adopted—product cost, product quality, market share and prestige, etc. What is the motive for tackling mechatronics?

Electronics, used to control mechanisms and provide a convenient interface between the product and the user, has the greatest increase in product content of any of the other areas in Fig. 1.4. Just as the motive for concurrent engineering is rooted in worldwide competition to reduce manufacturing cost while improving quality, the motive for mechatronics is a company's need to provide product features required by customers while making the most economical decisions between mechanical and electronic design solutions.

1.5.7 Funding and justification

What about funding? If a company is pursuing concurrent engineering or ISO 9000 audits, it may feel that it has spent enough money on corporatewide changes and has no more for mechatronics. However, as just discussed, tackling mechatronics can actually be done as part of these other initiatives. Also, applying mechatronics to product design typically has readily measurable paybacks.

For example, a coordinate measuring machine manufacturer has been able to achieve higher machine accuracies, and not by relying solely on increased precision of assemblies used to make their machine tools. Rather, they have added customized electronics that compensate for inaccuracies in machining parts of the equipment. By making trade-offs between mechanical solutions—increased precision in the parts—and electronic solutions—using cheap electronic ele-

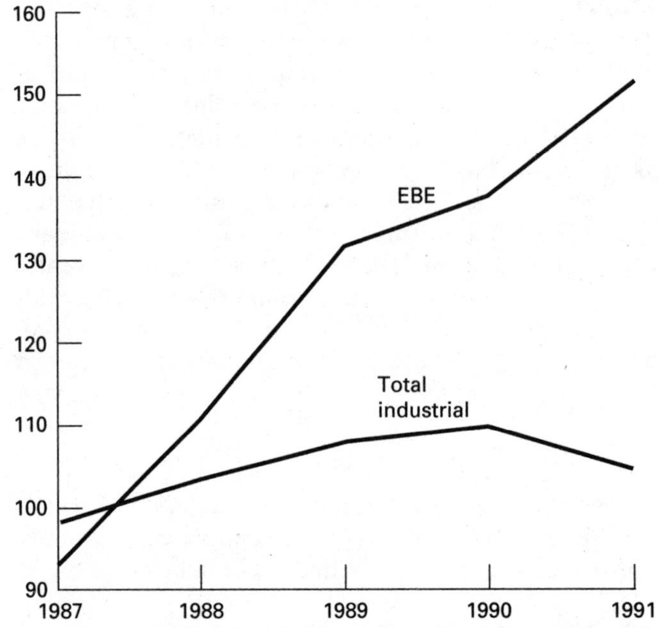

Figure 1.4 Electronic growth versus total industrial growth. EBE: electronic and business equipment.[10]

ments to give the necessary accuracies required in the final product. The net result is that total product costs are reduced.

References

1. Nevens, Summe, and Uttal: "Commercializing Technology: What the Best Companies Do," *Harvard Business Review,* May–June 1990, p. 154.
2. "History of Yasakawa," Yasakawa corporate records, Yasakawa Electric America, Inc.
3. "Defining Intel: 25 Years/25 Events," Intel Corporation Document #241730, 1993.
4. Comerford, Richard, Sr., Editor: "Mecha...what?" *IEEE Spectrum,* August 1994, p. 46.
5. Millbank, John, University of Salford: "Mecha-What," *Mechatronics Forum Newsletter,* No. 6, summer 1993.
6. Boothroyd, G.: *Assembly Engineering,* March 1982, pp. 42–45.
7. Boothroyd, G.: "Estimate Costs at an Early Stage," *American Machinist,* vol. 132, pp. 54–57, August 1988.
8. Clausing, Don: Concurrent Engineering, Massachusetts Institute of Technology, Design and Productivity International Conference, Honolulu, Hawaii, February 1991.
9. Flint, Jerry: "Empowered," *Forbes,* Feb. 15, 1993, p. 222.
10. *Electronic Business Forecast,* Cahners Publishing USA, May 6, 1991, pp. 1, 4, 6.

Chapter

2

Business Drivers

A manufacturer's business is driven by many factors. The number of issues is enormous and the rate of increase of the drivers is accelerating. Just for a minute, let's examine the automotive industry to see some of the drivers that manufacturers face every day. At one time, not too long ago, GM and Ford basically owned the U.S. automotive market. About twenty years ago the Japanese aggressively expanded their automotive capabilities beyond their region. The effect in the United States, and to a lesser extent in Europe, has been dramatic. Automobiles from halfway around the world can now be purchased at nearly equivalent to, and in some cases for less than, those manufactured in the United States. At first these imports were perceived to have inferior quality and have limited features. However, it did not take long for the Japanese to gain quality and functionality leadership over their U.S. and European rivals. Other countries have spawned automotive production for worldwide consumption, most notably Korean automotive manufacturers. At first quality and functionality were perceived to be inferior. However, in a few years, the Korean manufacturer Hyundai has erased most of the deficit.

GM and especially Ford have responded to some key drivers including quality and reliability, price, and time to market. In fact, as of early 1995, Chrysler is the recognized worldwide leader in new-car development.[1] Consider for a moment the Neon, Intrepid, and Cirrus. These products took less than 3 years from concept to market introduction. Why is it then that the Japanese still maintain a significant market share? A possible reason is that business has shifted somewhat from quality, reliability, and cost to other demands, such as making better use of people. Better use includes close cooperation mechanical, electrical, and software engineers. It is not a coincidence that the Japanese have led in the education and implementation of mechatronics. The business drivers will continue to change, and manufacturers must stay ahead of these demands if they are to compete. Consumer electronic manufacturers have to be alert since many of their product life cycles are under 1 year. This puts great pressure on the manufacturer to develop products quickly and effectively. A mechatronic approach provides the systematic method which will help nearly all manufacturers to be successful, since most products have mechanical, electrical, and software content.

Upon review of the automotive example and taking a broad view of the business drivers there are approximately a dozen key business drivers. These drivers affect the target markets, as well as product content and configuration. Some of the drivers have a greater effect on the target markets, while others more significantly affect the product content and configuration.

Each of the main drivers as shown in Fig. 2.1 will be explored to help gain an appreciation of what is affecting manufacturers today and their responses (products). Additionally, the effect that the business drivers have on the relationship between mechanical, electrical, and software engineers is discussed with a primary focus on why this relationship and a systematic process is a key to success.

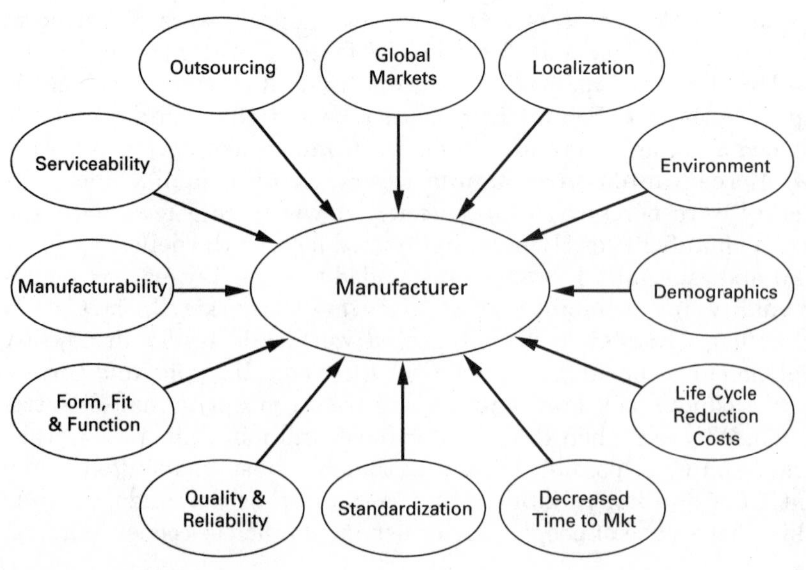

Figure 2.1 Key business drivers.

No manufacturer can blink for even a second, because the impact of a specific issue could be so conclusive as to alter the entire playing field which the manufacturer participates in or is planning to target.

2.1 Global Markets

Competition is pervasive for nearly all products. More specifically, there are worldwide suppliers and worldwide demand for most products. "Consumers in Bombay and Kiev demand Sonys..., just like everyone else. Same goes for industrial products and services, from AT&T's $5 million telephone switches to GE's $100 million large steam turbines."[1] It is therefore incumbent upon the manufacturer not to develop products in a vacuum, restricting availability to local markets or assuming the competitive threat is confined to their own country, hence the manufacturer must consider all markets and realize that competitive threats can arise anywhere throughout the world.

The cost of developing products is high, and continually rising. These development costs must be spread across as many products and geographic regions as possible. Spreading the costs across many markets can be achieved by forming international or national alliances. For example, Hewlett-Packard spreads risk across many products by using technology from its instrumentation business in several other markets such as oscilloscopes and cardiac analyzers.[2]

What are managers doing to increase the probability of their company's success? It seems that they are not focused on what it is going to take to be successful. "On average senior managers devote less than 3% of their time to building a *corporate* perspective on the future."[3] A large part of the future perspective is determining what markets to address and what the global competitive response may be. For the hypercompetitive, global 1990s, a question that most managers need to contemplate every day: Are you as good as the best in the world?

Of course, industries across the United States deal with global competition daily. Admittedly, some companies have fared better than others. The National Academy of Sciences and the Department of Defense detailed what it was going to take to make U.S. companies more competitive. These are serious improvements which must be made:[4]*

Reduce engineering design costs	15 to 30%
Decrease overall lead time	30 to 60%

---

*McDonald, Robert: "The Critical Importance of Database Management in Industrial Automation," *Proceedings of the 1990 ASME International Computers in Engineering,* Aug. 5–9, 1990, p. 131.

Increase productivity of manufacturing operation	40 to 70%
Reduce work in progress	30 to 60%

A key is to get employees to focus on the external market requirements and translate the requirements into a product response. The more the product team, which should include electrical, mechanical, and software engineers, understands the external and internal constraints, the greater the chance for success. Additionally, it is imperative that senior managers have a clear and shared understanding of how the industry that the manufacturer is a part of may be different in 10 years.[5]

2.2 Localization

As previously discussed, markets for products span the globe, and although the demand and requirements of a particular market for the "generic product" are essentially the same, the specifics that are required by the local market may be drastically different. For example, automobiles in England, Australia, and Hong Kong require right-side drives while automobiles in Canada, the United States, and Germany require left-side drives. This distinction is driven by the infrastructure of the local market. Needs specific to a particular market are also driven by the needs of the consumer of the local market.

It is imperative that manufacturers understand the needs of all local markets that they are trying to target. More importantly, any market may be a potential bonanza or mine field if the local market needs are not well understood. From the mechatronic perspective, the needs can be met by mechanical, electrical, and/or software capabilities. As the needs are translated into product features, the configuration of the particular product starts to take form.

These global needs introduce potential conflict between electrical, mechanical, and software engineering. It is critical that all the needs are captured and processed to determine the best method(s) to handle a particular requirement, be it an electrical, mechanical, or software capability. A particular customer requirement may therefore have multiple ways to address a need. Additionally, several requirements may have a mechanical capability to address one need and an electrical capability to address another need. The combination of mechanical, electrical, and software alternatives may be used in different combinations for different markets. Hence a conflict between the two methods, electrical and mechanical, may arise. This conflict must be resolved in an orderly fashion as early in the development cycle as possible; otherwise unnecessary costs will be introduced.

The needs of local markets may result in a significantly different product as compared to the "same" product available to another market, even though the "original" product was designed the same. Needless to say, the demands of local markets can be very rewarding or potentially very costly, and the right blend of mechanical, electrical, and software capabilities will affect the success of the product.

2.3 Environment

Environmental pressures are mounting and, in some cases, have reached a stage where a product must have a "green stamp," meaning the manufacturing process, as well as the product, must have minimal effect on the environment. Environmental requirements are insidious in all parts of the developed world including Asia, Australia, the United States, and Europe. Even in the underdeveloped regions of the world, environmental constraints are evident, and growing.

The effect on the products is significant in most industries. In Europe, for example the manufacturer must minimize the amount of packaging for a product such as foodstuffs. This is enforced by the fact that the manufacturer must take back packaging materials for recycling. The automobile industry is affected by recycling and pollution constraints. As an automotive supplier put it, "Federal regulations on our components keep our product line fluid. The products literally must change every two years or so."[6]

Products such as refrigerators and consumer electronics are being manufactured so that the product can be disassembled at the end of life for proper recycling. Printed circuit boards have been recycled for some time, primarily because of the value of the precious metals. Recycling is occurring now to save resources and landfill space.

Owing to the alternatives that a manufacturer may have to provide for product functionality, including mechanical, electrical, and software capabilities, the manufacturer has the opportunity to minimize the environmental effect. This can be accomplished only with foresight and with the cooperation of mechanical, electrical, and software engineers considering design, manufacturing, and service constraints early and often in the development cycle.

2.4 Demographics

The demographics throughout each country or region of the world provide another set of issues that the manufacturer must address to be successful. The population density among countries varies drastically. The makeup of the population also varies significantly from country to country. For example, the populations of the United States and Japan are aging quickly, to the point where the population aged over 50 is becoming the majority. In other countries such as Brazil, the bulk of the population is under the age of 30. It is important to consider the present status of the population and the future projections to fully understand the impact on the manufacturer. Each of these age groups has different needs that will impact the manufacturer's products. The needs are dictated by the level of education that a person may have, the person's exposure to technology, quality of life expectations, and the physical dexterity that the person may have or not have.[7]

The needs can be addressed by a variety of products. The product features can be achieved through the use of mechanical, electrical, and software capabilities. Certain people will be able to use the products and all of the features based on the individual person's knowledge of the technology, the physical restrictions that the person may have, and of course, the perceived value of the product and features. The manufacturer needs to achieve the right blend of mechanical, electrical, and software capabilities which will meet the target market. Naturally, the target market puts pressure on the development team to work together to optimize the capabilities from which they can select, be it mechanical, electrical, and/or software. In some cases, the features may be selectable depending on the needs of the customer. Again, the development team has a variety of capabilities from which to choose to address the need to have selectable features.

2.5 Life Cycle Reduction and Costs

The product life cycle, defined as the time from concept to retirement, for most products is decreasing (see Figs. 2.2 through 2.4). In

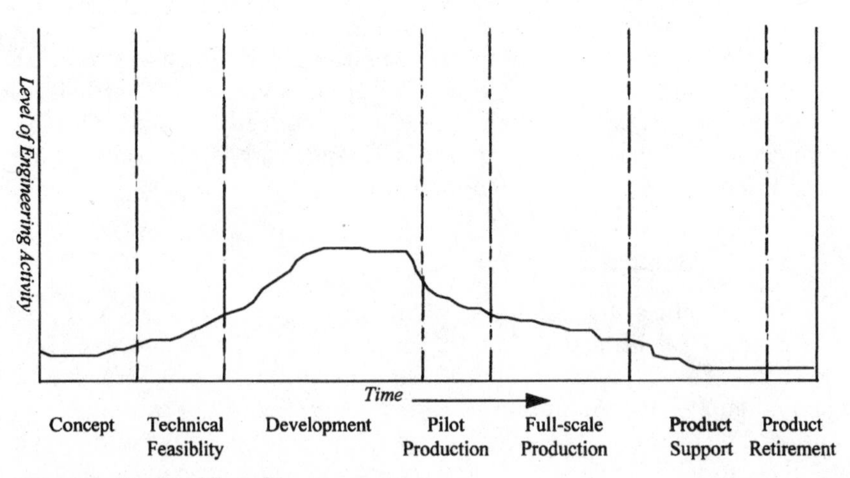

Figure 2.2 Product life cycle.

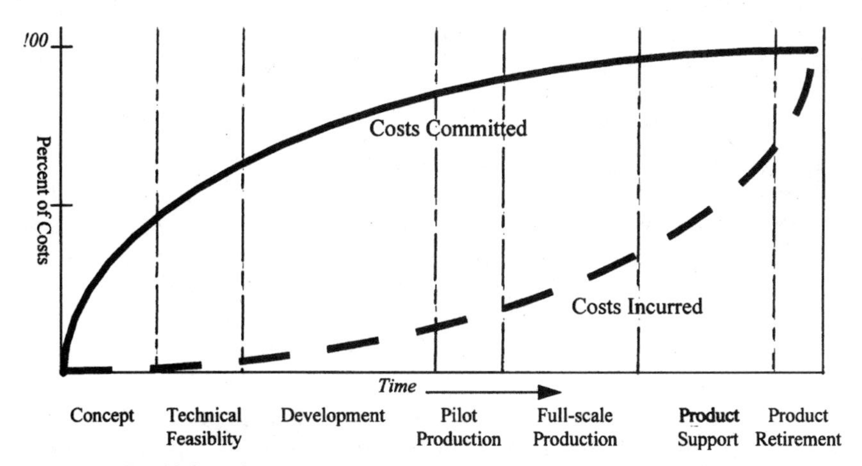

Figure 2.3 Total life cycle cost.

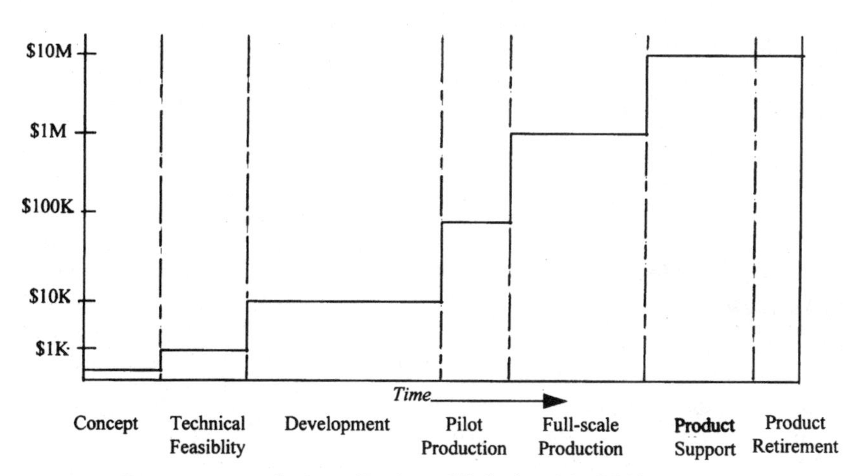

Figure 2.4 Rise in costs with time. (*Business Week, Apr. 30, 1990.*)

some cases, the life cycle is decreasing at a significant pace because of the demands of the consumer and new technologies which continue to be introduced at a dizzying pace. Some of the evolution is needed to increase the usefulness of a particular product, while further evolutions are needed to attack the cost of producing or servicing the product, and still more evolution helps make the product look and feel better.

Much impact on the product life cycle is due to the fact that people want more and more functionality for a particular product. Some of this functionality is absolutely necessary, while some that is being requested is based solely on convenience. Many manufacturers are purposely shortening the product life cycle to introduce new products quickly in an attempt to increase competitiveness.

Therefore, the need for the manufacturer to quickly understand the customer's needs and the competitive threat to develop a product quickly is the key to the manufacturer's success. The ability to quickly consider and integrate electrical, software, and mechanical environments over the product life cycle from design to manufacturing to service will provide significant leverage to compete in an atmosphere of short product life cycles.

Life cycles are getting shorter. Additionally, each phase of the life cycle is correspondingly shorter. The graph represents the amount of engineering activity for each of the phases. It stands to reason, therefore, that mechanical, electrical, and software engineers must work in cooperation to yield shorter development cycles. More importantly decisions made early in the development have a dramatic effect on the total life cycle cost of the product including manufactured and service costs as shown in Fig. 2.3. For example, if a mechanical engineer defines a housing irrespective of the electronic components that are part of the housing, then the ability to assemble and service those components will, in all probability, be difficult and therefore expensive.

If mechanical, electrical, and software engineers continue to work in sequence, the chance to reduce the development time decreases significantly. Furthermore, if the engineers do not cooperate, the cost to make a change later in the process rises exponentially, as shown in Fig. 2.3. The cost to make changes is relatively inexpensive in the concept and technical feasibility stages. If changes are required in production or after the product has been delivered to the customer, the costs to the manufacturer are extremely prohibitive.

Hence it is extremely important that mechanical, electrical, and software engineers work in an interactive team environment to make the changes and trade-offs early in the development cycle, preferably in the concept or technical feasibility stages.

2.6 Decreased Time to Market

This issue, although touched upon in Secs. 2.1 and 2.5, warrants a separate discussion because of its importance to competitiveness. Since product life cycles are short and getting shorter, combined with the fact that base technologies are readily available, companies must get a product to market as quickly as possible. It is paramount to the company's livelihood. Having a short time to market often enables a company to be first to market, and generally commands a price premium. For example, in the European car radio market, the first to market can charge a 20 percent premium.[8] The ability to charge a premium lasts only until competitors introduce equivalent products.

Unfortunately, many managers fail to recognize the benefits of getting a product to market first. The program manager is more concerned with keeping the project at or below budget, most of the time at the expense of slowing the development down. What managers do not realize is that late market entry significantly affects profits. In contrast, the profitability associated with being first to market more than offsets the cost of being over budget. For example, assume the market grows at 20 percent per year, prices drop 12 percent per year, and the life cycle is 5 years, launching a product 6 months late can reduce the cumulative profits generated by the product by one-third. To contrast, using the same set of assumptions, a cost overrun of 30 percent for the project will reduce cumulative profits by approximately 3 percent.[8]

It stands to reason that manufacturers need to be focused on ensuring time market entry of their products and that remaining competitive requires decreased time to market. This has a tremendous effect on the development team. Often, because of budgetary reasons, the team is not authorized from the project initiation to have mechanical, electrical, and software engineers. Additionally, manufacturing and service engineering are not included until late in the development. Changes are inevitably needed in the traditional scenario, and these changes are expensive. Furthermore changes take time, and if iterations are needed between mechanical and electrical engineering the time to market is going to be severely affected. How can this be avoided or at least significantly reduced? Mechanical, electrical, and software engineers need to work in close cooperation as early in the development cycle as possible. Their cooperative efforts will enable many of the constraints to be considered simultaneously, reducing development time and ultimately decreasing time to market.

2.7 Standardization

Historically, each country set its own standards, which in many cases conflicted with each other. Some countries' standards made it prohibitive for companies to enter markets because the volume for the particular product may not have warranted the cost to modify the original product. Countries are now working to create international standards organizations such as ISO (International Standards Organization) and IEC (International Electrotechnical Commission). "ISO is an international federation of 100 national standards organizations. It has established over 8700 standards, covering all fields except electrical and electronic engineering, which is the domain of its sister organization, the IEC."[9]

Advocates say that standards facilitate trade between countries. International standards facilitate more competition since modifications specific to local countries are not needed. This enables market entry by potentially more competitors, making international trade easier. The harmonization of standards means that engineers won't have to return to ground zero each time a new country is added as a target market.

Standardization is in direct contrast to a previously discussed issue, localization, where local culture may dictate slightly different features of a given base product. However, standards may act in a similar fashion to localization issues if a manufacturer is unable to meet the standard. Given this scenario, it is unlikely that the manufacturer will last long in today's competitive environment.

For the development team trying to address standards, it may mean more time to document the design or determine alternative designs. The alternative design can be a combination of mechanical, electrical, and software capabilities depending on the market requirements and standards. Nonetheless the team must be cognizant of mechanical, electrical, and software international standards to reduce unnecessary iterations during development or, worse, at later stages in the product life cycle. The required modifications to meet the standards could be subtle or could be significant.

For example, a train manufacturer had to incorporate a redesign in order to meet international standards for mechanical and electromechanical design.[10] Further, at a washing machine manufacturer, Bosch-Siemens, engineers redesigned a high-end washing machine to include electronic controls so that the machine would comply with electromagnetic standards.[9] These redesigns were costly because the products required design iterations. However, some redesign may be unavoidable, since a standard may go into effect after a specific version of the product has been released. Project managers of design teams need to check for all standards and proposed standards that may apply to the project. Existing practices will need to be checked against the standards. The more that this effort is coordinated between disciplines—mechanical, electrical, and software engineering, early in the development cycle the less costly the development will be.

2.8 Quality and Reliability

High levels of quality and low amounts of defective products are a prerequisite just to gain entry into the competitive environment. The quality thrust over the last decade has enabled most manufacturers to achieve the level of quality of Japanese manufacturers. It is expected that a product, any product, will have high quality and reliability levels.

Most companies have progressed from the early quality thrusts to a point where quality is no longer just a program but is embedded as part of the organization's culture. In fact, 70 percent of the companies in a Manufacturing Attitudes Survey conducted by Benchmark Research claimed to be implementing TQM (total quality management), and 63 percent say they use SPC (statistical process control).[11] For the purpose of clarity, "SPC seeks to monitor and correct drifts in quality during the manufacturing processes, starting with a thorough knowledge of the link between them and the product defects. TQM applies a set of principles to focus continuous attention on quality at every step of the design, development, and manufacturing by everyone in the country. TQM's overriding purpose is to increase value to customers."[12]

It is clear that the global marketplace and global competition have helped increase the overall quality competence of most manufacturers. Most customers demand that the product be extremely reliable over longer periods than in the past. Furthermore, customers require that a product be reliable over the entire life cycle of the product until the product is disposed of. Clearly, high quality and high reliability are not the competitive advantages they once were for some manufacturers. "By the year 2000, quality will be the price of market entry, not a competitive differentiator."[3]

Each of the team members, mechanical, electrical, and software engineers need to understand the quality and reliability of the particular components, assemblies, or software programs they may develop. Additionally, and equally important, each needs to understand the quality and reliability implications of the entire design. This close cooperation needs to occur as early in the development cycle as possible. Alternatives can be pursued. For example, the team may select a mechanical assembly because it is projected to have higher quality and reliability as opposed to an electronic and software alternative. The reverse is also a possibility. The team may select the electronic and software alternative over the mechanical alternative based on projected higher quality and reliability. Of course, the selection should be made not just on the quality and reliability, but by considering all the related issues discussed in this chapter.

2.9 Form, Fit, and Function

The configuration of a product is dictated by what functionality is needed to meet the customer needs and what size and shape will meet the customer requirements. At the disposal of the development team are a plethora of choices to meet the customer requirements of form, fit, and function. Specifically, the required customer functionality can be addressed with electrical components, mechanical components, or software routines. Each alternative has an associated size. Each assembly has a specific size and shape. The combination of assemblies must fit together to form the end product. Additionally, each alternative has corresponding quality, reliability, manufacturing, and serviceability constraints which are discussed in this chapter.

The key, therefore, is to select the combination of functionality that minimizes cost and size, eases manufacturing and serviceability, and has a high level of quality and reliability. Hence there must be a coordinated effort to consider electrical, mechanical, and software alternatives available to the team to meet the product requirements. Functional requirements include what features are required by the customer and what performance is desired of the product.

For example, copiers made 10 years ago coordinated the light source and the system to apply the toner with a moving piece of paper (the copy).[13] This required technology:

- To mechanically move the paper
- To coordinate and focus the light source and lens
- To apply and fuse the toner

Competing in the copier market meant creating innovations in the above areas. However, additional competence is needed in other technology areas such as:

- Control hardware and software
- Photoreceptors
- Panel displays

Companies will risk producing a product that is not competitive if they fall behind in one area.[8] This scenario is prevalent in all industries.

The need is to create a product which optimally addresses the demanded features requiring a coordinated effort between mechanical, electrical, and software engineers since many of the features can be addressed in several ways. Furthermore, the product configuration needs to be optimized so that the product is competitive. Optimization can occur only if all the alternatives are understood and there is a systematic approach to evaluate the alternatives and select the best combination. How does this happen? A mechatronic approach must be utilized.

2.10 Manufacturability

Manufacturing of a product and its components and assemblies is key to its success (including market acceptance and profitability). Hence the objective is to strive for the minimum practical manufacturing cost. As such, the product, its components and assemblies must be designed for manufacturability and assembly. This needs to happen early in the development cycle where manufacturing engineers work with the development team. Manufacturability applies to both electrical and mechanical components and assemblies.

Mechanical, electrical, and software engineers need some way to evaluate the effect that their design may have on manufacturing and service (to be addressed next). Notice the emphasis on "their design," not the impact of mechanical components and assemblies and then the effect electrical components and assemblies have on manufacturing. The manufacturability and assembly evaluation, in general terms, is based on whether a separate part is needed or part functionality can be combined; ease of handling, feeding, and orienting; and ease of assembly. Desired functionality may be satisfied by several alternatives. The following is a more comprehensive design for manufacturability set of guidelines for designers to consider:

- Design with a minimum number of parts.
- Develop a modular design.
- Minimize part variations.
- Design parts to be multifunctional (include electrical and mechanical capabilities).
- Design parts for multiuse.
- Design parts for ease of fabrication.
- Avoid separate fasteners.
- Minimize assembly directions.

- Maximize compliance (of parts); design for ease of assembly.
- Minimize handling.
- Evaluate assembly methods.
- Eliminate or simplify adjustments.
- Avoid flexible components.

These criteria should be used to determine the optimum alternatives which satisfy the feature requirements, from a manufacturability and assembly point of view. The alternatives consist of mechanical, electrical, and software capabilities, or combinations of all capabilities. The team must not lose sight of the system for the components. In other words, optimizing an assembly without considering the consequences on the system may very well suboptimize the system. Remember that manufacturability is but one of the criteria; there are other criteria which must be used to select the "right" combination of electrical, mechanical, and software capabilities.

2.11 Serviceability

A relatively new idea is becoming prevalent for manufacturers to deal with to increase competitiveness—product serviceability. As discussed earlier, customers are looking at the entire life cycle cost of the products they purchase. The life cycle cost includes the original purchase price, the price of any upgrades to the product, and the price of service to maintain the product. "Serviceability of a product can and should take the lead in maintaining customer satisfaction."[14] Actually, superior service can lead to customer preference, creating an unbeatable competitive advantage. The objective of design for serviceability is twofold:[14]

1. As a method for development teams to consider serviceability during early design concept definition
2. As a method for service professionals to identify the warranty costs of their products

Serviceability, like most of the business drivers discussed in this chapter, should be considered at the very beginning of the product life cycle in the design concept stage. By doing the analysis up-front, problems, solutions, and costs can be identified when the cost of modification can be minimized. Unfortunately, the idea of considering serviceability at the design concept stage is very radical to many companies, though it is gaining support quickly. "Serviceability is the next major hurdle to further improve Ford's overall quality and provide greater customer benefits."[14]

The effect of serviceability on the customer is profound. First of all, if a product requires service, the customer is generally not pleased. However, there is a significant opportunity to recapture the customer's trust if the customer has a good service experience. This good experience is highly dependent on the serviceability of the product. If the problem is easy to service, the amount of time the product is "out of commission" is minimized, and the less costly the repair is, in general. Customer satisfaction is probably achieved in this scenario. However, if the product is difficult to service, then the product is "out of commission" longer and the repair is more costly. Most assuredly, customers will be more unhappy than when they brought the product in for service.

Mechanical, electrical, and software engineers are a key to the success of the serviceability of a product. They need to understand that serviceability is critical in the eyes of the customer. As such, alternatives can be evaluated for serviceability with the entire system in mind, not just the individual assemblies. What Ford is trying to do is to "broaden the engineer's objectives and make designing for service part of a total set of priorities."[14]

2.12 Outsourcing/Task Sourcing

More and more companies are realizing that manufacturing their own assemblies and components has become prohibitively expensive. The technology used by most components and assemblies is advancing at a dizzying pace. The cost to stay current is very high, including capital outlays, labor costs, and costs to train personnel on the new technology. Many companies are deciding that their best alternative is to focus on the core competencies and outsource the rest. The outsourcing or task sourcing includes not only the component and assembly manufacturing but the engineering to develop the components and assemblies. "Today, many firms set-up as component manufacturers must demonstrate their competence as producers of components and systems designed by them to meet the needs of the OEM (original equipment manufacturer)."[15]

Another factor in the requirement to outsource is the attempt to reduce the number of suppliers that a manufacturer uses. Instead of component suppliers, what is being demanded is system integrators—suppliers who provide systems and solutions rather than just components. This requirement forces suppliers to assume additional responsibility to integrate the system into the end product.

The benefits of outsourcing are pretty obvious. Component and assembly costs are reduced. The number of suppliers is reduced. Most importantly, "It promotes more teaming at all levels, which results in doing it right the first time."[6]

Outsourcing leads to a total system approach, which is what a mechatronic approach preaches. Outsourcing basically requires a mechatronic approach to be most successful. All disciplines must work together to get the system to work right the first time. This includes electrical, mechanical, and software engineers from both the OEM and its suppliers considering the entire product life cycle requirements.

2.13 Conclusion

All the issues or constraints described in this chapter must be considered by the manufacturer if the manufacturer wants to survive in the global marketplace. These issues will drive the success or failure of the development team. To increase success, a mechatronic approach must be employed where electrical, mechanical, and software engineers work closely starting in the early phases of the development cycle, considering all product life cycle constraints—functionality required, manufacturability, and serviceability.

Products are the manufacturer's response to the business drivers. Therefore, the content of the products which are being developed and the process to increase the success of their development are discussed in the next chapter.

References

1. Sherman, Stratford: "Are You as Good as the Best in the World," *Fortune,* Dec. 13, 1993, p. 95.
2. Nevens, Summe, and Uttal: "Commercializing Technology: What the Best Companies Do," *Harvard Business Review,* May–June 1990, p. 158.
3. Hamel and Prahalad: "Competing for the Future," *Harvard Business Review,* July–August 1994, p. 123.
4. McDonald, Robert: "The Critical Importance of Database Management in Industrial Automation," *Proceedings of the 1990 ASME International Computers in Engineering,* Aug. 5–9, 1990, p. 131.
5. Hamel and Prahalad: "Competing for the Future," *Harvard Business Review,* July–August 1994, p. 122.
6. LeDuc and Hogan: "Outsourcing Changes the Engineering Lineup," *Design News,* Oct. 10, 1994, p. 128.
7. "Manufacturing into the Late 1990's," PA Consulting Group Report for DTI.
8. Nevens, Summe, and Uttal: "Commercializing Technology: What the Best Companies Do," *Harvard Business Review,* May–June 1990, p. 157.
9. Hars, Adele: "Global Standards Change the Face of Product Design," *Design News,* Sept. 26, 1994, p. 24.
10. Hars, Adele: "Global Standards Change the Face of Product Design," *Design News,* Sept. 26, 1994, p. 23.

11. Computervision: "Concurrent Engineering," *Contact,* Summer 1992, p. 10.
12. Shina, Sammy: "New Rules for World-Class Companies," *IEEE Spectrum,* July 1991, p. 25.
13. Nevens, Summe, and Uttal: "Commercializing Technology: What the Best Companies Do," *Harvard Business Review,* May–June 1990, p. 159.
14. Teresko, John: "Service Now Is a Design Element," *Industry Week,* Feb. 7, 1994.
15. LeDuc and Hogan: "Outsourcing Changes the Engineering Lineup," *Design News,* Oct. 10, 1994, p. 122.

Chapter

3

Product Content vs. Process

The primary focus of this book is to detail a systematic process, a mechatronic approach, necessary to increase the success of getting products to market which meet the target market, and to detail how to implement a mechatronic approach. To further understand the need for a mechatronic approach, it is useful to review the products that are available today and the contents of the products. Furthermore, it is important to discuss the trends in product content over the past years, to help predict the future trends.

For just a minute, ponder the products that are available today for the individual or an organization—automobiles, jet aircraft, robots, CNC machinery, stereos, computers, televisions, radar systems, and refrigerators. Strikingly, most products have a combination of electrical, mechanical, and software components or assemblies to meet customer requirements. Furthermore, the mix of these capabilities is increasing as manufacturers scramble to meet the burgeoning needs of their customers. The complexity of the products is also increasing. Some products have a larger percentage of electrical components and assemblies, such as televisions and radar systems. Other products have more mechanical components and assemblies such as machinery. Still other products such as computers contain significant software content as well as electronic content. Each of the types of content provides specific functionality from which the development team can select to meet the target market requirements. In order to make the trade-offs to optimize the product, a systematic process is needed. However, an interesting question arises—does the product content drive the process? or does the process drive the product content? To explore this question, the different types of product content and the corresponding functionality that the content provides will be explored. The mechatronic process is introduced in order to determine the relationship between product and process.

3.1 Product Content

Customer requirements ultimately drive the need for a combination of electrical, mechanical, and software components and assemblies. Nearly all products are comprised of components, assemblies, and systems. The number of components and assemblies and the complexity of the contents depend on the complexity of the product and its associated features. The relationship between components, assemblies, systems, and end products is represented in Fig. 3.1.

At the lowest level of the product hierarchy are electrical, mechanical components. Moving up the hierarchy, assemblies are comprised of components and assemblies are combined to create systems. Finally end products are determined from a combination of systems. Furthermore, at the lowest level of the hierarchy there are more components than at the system level. It becomes very evident when viewing the hierarchy that ultimately all components come together to comprise the product. Hence market success increasingly depends on the ability of the manufacturer to integrate electronics and computing technologies into a wide range of traditionally mechanical products.

The product component hierarchy helps illustrate the need for all disciplines, especially mechanical, electrical, and software engineers, to work together at all levels of product definition. Ultimately, the team effort should begin at the component level to understand the constraints of each discipline as it relates to fit, manufacturability, performance, and service.

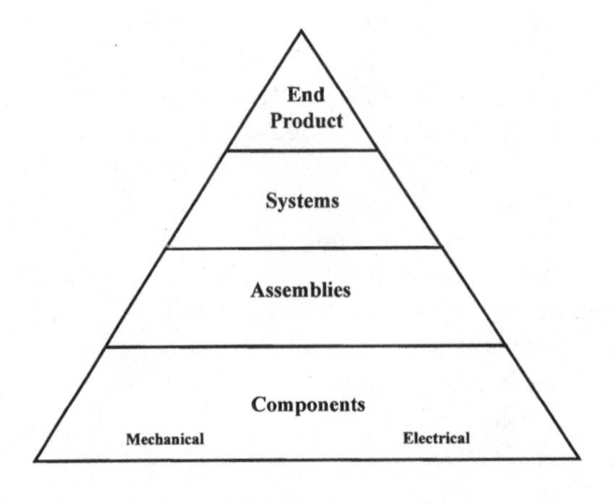

Figure 3.1 Product hierarchy.

3.1.1. Product component types

3.1.1.1 Mechanical components. A mechanical component or assembly can be defined as a component or assembly that has physical characteristics such as length, width, height, and mass. Mechanical components provide the structure to house functionality, provide rigidity, enable physical stability, and provide aesthetics. It gives the product substance and determines fit constraints and form. Additionally, mechanical components can be combined into an assembly and provide functionality such as that provided in a piston, crankshaft, and cylinder walls.

Examples of mechanical components and assemblies include structural interior and exterior of automobiles, a jet aircraft fuselage, a washing machine housing, and the exterior case of a CD player.

Some of the concerns regarding a mechanical component or assembly include whether the structure, enclosure, etc., is rigid enough to withstand the working environment of the product. If the structure is not rigid or solid, the product or other components or assemblies, such as printed circuit boards, could be damaged and therefore the product, in all likelihood, will not function properly. This protection needs to extend to protecting the product from being crushed, damaged because of a fall, or contaminated by a harsh liquid contaminant.

Therefore, the mechanical component or assembly is the "protective outer skin" or package for the product as well as providing structure to house other components and assemblies. Housing other components and assemblies leads to a larger question: How do all the components and assemblies fit together? More specifically, what is the relationship with the electrical components? How does the package affect the electrical components and how do the electrical components and assemblies affect the package? Concerns include:

1. Is there enough space between electrical components to ensure there is not electrical interference? Is the package large enough to accommodate properly located electrical components?
2. What materials and configuration are needed to address rigidity and provide shock resistance for the electrical components and assemblies?
3. What shape and size of package will be able to house all the components and assemblies?
4. Where should vents be located to enable cooling?
5. How can the weight be minimized?

6. How can the center of gravity be balanced for automotive, aerospace, and consumer electronics products?

Additionally, other items in the product life cycle, namely, manufacturability and serviceability, must be considered when determining the package. Some of the major concerns which must be addressed are as follows:

1. Can the package, as defined, be manufactured?
2. Can the assemblies and components housed by the package be easily assembled and disassembled?
3. What special equipment will be required to assemble and fit the components and assemblies into the package?
4. Is the combination of components and assemblies of the highest quality?
5. Can the package, and the components and assemblies that it houses, be easily serviced?

3.1.1.2 Electrical components. An electrical component can be defined as a component that consumes, stores, processes, or produces eletricity. Furthermore, a large portion of today's electrical components process logical instructions. Electrical components provide the "intelligence" for the product. The electronic components and assemblies detect, provide feedback, and modify operating characteristics of the product. "Electronics, born with the research into electrical energy sources, rose with its application to the 20th century electrical appliances and with the use of signals in communications. Electronics has moved from research...to the control and management of signals."[1] The importance and abundance of electronic capabilities in today's products is increasing at a dizzying pace. It does not appear that the pace is going to subside; if anything it will probably increase.

A printed circuit board is an electrical component. The electrical component of a missile is the avionics, guidance, and actuation systems.[2*] Power supplies, small board computers, I/O boards, relays, and programmable logic controllers are examples of electrical components.

What is the effect on mechanical components and assemblies? The impact can be significant in a couple of ways. First, adding electronic capability to a mechanical system often simplifies the resulting mechanical system by reducing the number of components and moving parts.

---

*Atkinson and Glasscook: "An Implementation of a Product Data Management System," *Proceedings of the ASME International Computers in Engineering,* August 1990, p. 37.

This simplification is accomplished by transferring complex functionality such as accurate positioning from the mechanical system to the electronics. Second, adding electronics enables functionality that otherwise would have been unachievable. An example of this is antilock brakes for automobiles, a speed sensor which in turn adjusts the pulse of brake force while braking on slippery surfaces. Additionally, the electronic content affects the mechanical design in many previously identified ways. It is incumbent upon the development team to select an alternative which minimizes the effects on the mechanical components and yet meets the customer needs. Trade-offs will need to be made. Specific trade-offs are addressed in a later section of this chapter.

Another key issue is how the electronic components are going to be interconnected to ensure integrity of the electronic systems. Addressing this question needs to occur early in the development, because the effect on the final product could be significant. Typically the location of interconnects is determined after product is largely designed. In many cases there is not enough room for the interconnecting cables or harnesses to be added to the product. For example, what type of interconnections will be used, multicore cables or ribbon cables or wire harnesses? These require space and may possibly affect the performance of adjacent electronic components and assemblies. These interconnections cannot just be "stuffed in" at the end of the development cycle or, worse, determined during pilot production.

When determining the electronic content required for a product driven by a set of customer needs, it is critical to understand the relationship the stages of the product life cycle have on the development. Ease of manufacturing and servicing are keys to the overall product success. This is also true of interconnections, since assembly and service is generally very difficult.

3.1.1.3 Software components and control components. Software is defined as the routines and logical instructions to be interpreted by the electrical components. Examples include programs such as Microsoft Excel, "C" programming language, and graphical user interfaces. The electrical components and assemblies combined with software capabilities provide the bulk of functionality of "intelligence" in today's products. They are inextricably tied together. There are varying degrees of software capabilities, or control functionality.

One of the primary concerns of the design team is that of the person-machine interface—how the product form can be used to implement the functions required by the product user. For example, there are multiple ways for a driver to steer a car—through a tiller attached directly to the wheel mechanism, through a wheel that indirectly controls the wheels through linkages, through power assistance provided by hydraulics, or through a wheel that provides input to a configurable servocontroller. Each of these forms allows the driver to perform the function of steering the car.

The decision-making process at the man-machine interface level actually should consider a variety of solutions that would allow the product to function successfully. Trade-off analysis can than be performed to select the superior solution based on a variety of criteria.

Typically there will be several iterations between the person-machine stage of the design and the internal form-function design. This is typical when there is a technological advance that allows the end product forms and functions to be implemented more cost-effectively, with higher quality or with more functions. These iterations in the design process set the stage for the actual control methodology to provide the desired functionality.

Customers detail the functions that they want performed by the product. The design team decides how these functions are to be implemented, thus establishing the form of the product. Within this space defined by the function and form of the product there is a wide range of control alternatives. However, these control alternatives are largely limited based on the nature of the functions and forms used in the implementation. Consider the following product requirement:

> The product must allow the user to turn the wheels of the car using a device located in the car. This product must allow the user to respond quickly to adverse road conditions even when the wheels are subject to adverse lateral forces.

Twenty years ago the product requirement would have been accomplished by using linkages that drive a gear, with further linkages out to the front wheels of the car. Consider the change to the above requirement today.

> The product must allow the user to turn the wheels as above and additionally...change the amount of oversteering delivered to the wheels while driving at high speeds. It must also allow for a "sport" and "standard" steering style which alters the characteristics of the steering at all speeds.

The current form of this implementation is still to put a steering wheel in the driver's hands, but this time the steering mechanism is monitored by an on-board computer. The steering conditions provide input to a control algorithm which in turn drives the linkages depending on the conditions. The linkages are stiffened for high-speed cornering, for example. The manufacturer develops the control software and has the opportunity to allow the software to behave in various ways depending on other inputs from the driver. This mechatronic implementation allowed the product designers to either solve customer's requests for function or add new features that would be a competitive advantage.

3.2 Process

As stated throughout, the overall objective is to implement a process that can get products to market as quickly as possible which meet customer requirements and that considers constraints of the product life cycle. Companies that are considered the leaders in minimizing total cost of products with electrical, mechanical, and software content such as Sony and Xerox have utilized a process geared toward developing products considering all constraints as early as possible. In effect, they have executed a mechatronic process. Each of these companies has implemented a focused development process, and although it was not termed mechatronics, the results were a mechatronic approach. As products evolve, more and more functionality is required in smaller packages, requiring a balance of capabilities in a systematic process. An ad hoc process, which has been used, will not be successful, especially as competitive pressures increase. Hence the need to have a process that has a mechatronic focus is paramount today and will become more important in the future. A process which ensures that electrical, mechanical, and software capabilities are balanced is outlined in this section.

Upon review of the products that are manufactured today, it is apparent that the functionality, complexity, and aesthetics have increased. At the same time, the increased quality and reliability requirements have not subsided. Next, the product must be easy to manufacture to minimize the product cost, and last, the product must be serviceable. In short, customers care about the total cost over the product life cycle. The total life cycle cost is the product development and manufacturing cost, plus the cost to implement the product, and the service and maintenance costs. The total cost is significantly affected by the product complexity, functionality, and aesthetics. The more complex the product, generally the more costly the product is to develop, manufacture, and service.

The response to create a formalized process was predicated on the product requirements and technology acceleration. Therefore, the product content has, in most cases, dictated the need for a process. The content required for most products requires a different approach to ensure the success (market acceptance) of the products being developed. Therefore, the product content drove the need for a complementary process. This process is a mechatronic approach. The good news, therefore, is that it is not too late to implement a mechatronic process.

In fact, if manufacturers implement a mechatronic process now, they still have the opportunity to create a competitive advantage.

3.2.1 Mechatronic process

The mechatronic process is evolving. The process has the flexibility to respond to a given set of constraints including customer requirements and life cycle considerations, while at the same time enabling trade-offs to take place between electrical, mechanical, and software capabilities. The strength of the process is just that, the ability to balance the capabilities given a set of constraints. The key to the process is to ensure the balance of the capabilities as early in the development cycle as possible. To achieve this the old boundaries between electrical, mechanical, and software engineers must be removed so that the entire product is looked at from a multidisciplinary approach early in and throughout the development cycle.

The balance via trade-offs of electrical, mechanical, and software capabilities based on a set of customer and product life cycle constraints is depicted in Fig. 3.2.

3.2.1.1 Concept stage. A mechatronic process starts from input regarding customer requirements, usually via marketing or sales. These requirements include a list of functions and features required. The response to customer requirements is some kind of product which has yet to be defined. In some cases, the product definition may be an adaptation to an existing product or a response to an existing competi-

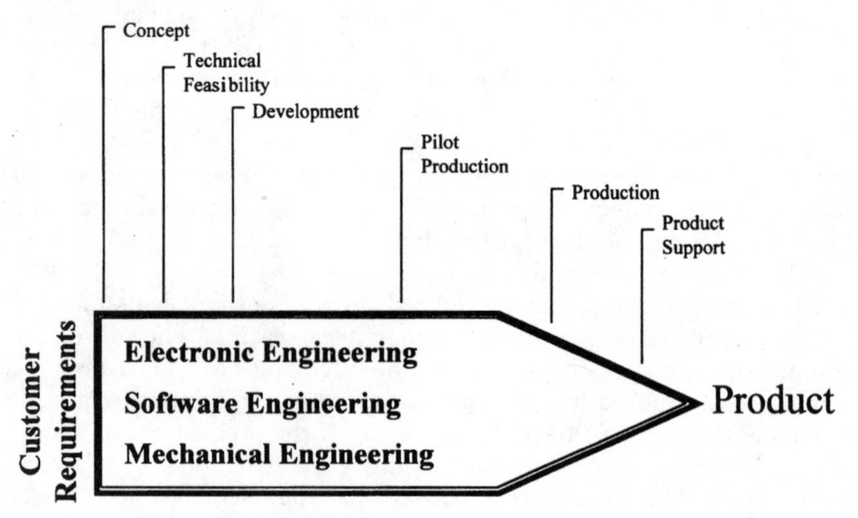

Figure 3.2 Mechatronic approach.

tive product. To capture and evaluate the customer requirements and create a well-defined product specification, it is suggested that a QFD (Quality Function Deployment) analysis be performed. Briefly defined, a "QFD relates subjective customers' desires (called customer attributes or CAs) to quantitative engineering characteristics (ECs). By conducting a QFD, an engineering team finds out which customer attributes are important (because either the customer wants them or the competition has them) and the set of engineering characteristics to be addressed to improve each customer attribute."[3] An important part of the mechatronic approach is that the team conducting the QFD, or customer requirement analysis and product specification, needs to include the electrical, mechanical, and software engineers, as shown in Fig. 3.2 at the concept stage. Traditionally, the team did not include the multidisciplined representation, and as such the risk of product failure was higher. The manufacturer has the opportunity to correct this problem using a mechatronic approach from the get go.

3.2.1.2 Technical feasibility stage. Upon completion of the product specification and the resulting concept confirmation, the next step is to prove the technical feasibility. The team has much technology to choose from, whether it be generally accepted technology or in-house developed technology. The objective is to preliminarily select the technologies which fulfill the product specification. It is at this stage that trade-off analysis is important to balance the optimum technology alternatives which meet the customer requirements and fulfill the product specification. This trade-off analysis needs to be interactive versus sequential, with team members including mechanical, electrical, and software engineers, considering the life cycle constraints, to determine the optimum balance of the different technological alternatives. Additionally, potential suppliers for each of the alternative technologies need to be involved to assist the trade-off analysis. Their input and the effect on cost will be invaluable.

3.2.1.2.1 Trade-off analysis. In the highly competitive global marketplace, the divisions between electrical and mechanical engineering need to be increasingly replaced by an integrated and interdisciplinary approach. This is fostered by mechatronics. Trade-offs need to occur as early in development as possible. The trade-off between form, fit, and function has not traditionally occurred until the prototype has been completed or, worse, when the product has begun production. As discussed earlier, modifications are very expensive to make at the pilot and production stages of the development. Hence these expenses can be minimized if the constraints or trade-offs are considered earlier in the development process.

The development team has many options available to meet customer requirements, including mechanical, electrical, and software capabilities. Hopefully, these options are combined and balanced to meet the customer requirements. The goal is to select the options that will provide the most functionality possible in a pleasing package that will protect the product under normal working conditions. In short, trade-offs need to be made between the functionality desired and the package in which it must fit. This trade-off can cause significant friction between engineering disciplines since the responsibility for the package definition falls in the hands of the mechanical engineer, and logic and intelligence of the product is in the electrical engineers' domain.

3.2.1.2.2 Manufacturability, assembly, and serviceability analysis. As discussed in Chap. 2, manufacturability and assembly constraints are prevalent. The earlier in the development process that manufacturability and assembly constraints are defined for each of the alternatives the more successful and efficient the product development will be. It is imperative that the manufacturability constraints be considered when the trade-off analysis is performed.

3.2.1.2.2.1 Manufacturability. Each of the components has an associated process to manufacture the component. The technology to manufacture the component or assembly plays a large role in determining the final cost. Manufacturability concerns include:

- Can the component be molded in the shape and configuration that is desired, providing enough venting to enable cooling?
- Can the component or assembly be manufactured so that it can be easily assembled to other components?
- Is the defined printed circuit board easy to manufacture? What will be the density of the board to enable effective component insertion? What percentage of components can be autoinserted?
- What process will be used to form the metal component?

3.2.1.2.2.2 Assembly and disassembly. The greatest impact on assembly and disassembly costs is achieved through the reduction of board assemblies and parts to be assembled and disassembled. Thus a unit is designed which is easy to assemble and disassemble.

There is significant effect on the manufacturing process by ensuring the product can be easily assembled. Additionally, assembly is facilitated by ensuring components and assemblies are easily accessible. There is significant effect on serviceability if assembly, accessibility, and disassembly requirements are considered.

Assembly and disassembly guidelines include:

- The unit should require minimal (none preferred) rotation to disassemble or assemble the unit. This enables the repair personnel to use the minimum amount of motion to disassemble and assemble the unit.
- Eliminate internal cabling wherever possible because cabling requires connectors and connectors are prone to problems such as misconnection.
- Utilize fasteners which are easy to snap on and snap off. Fasteners are the preferred method for attachment.
- Minimize the number of screws. If screws must be used, a standard screw must be used throughout the unit so that the same tool can be used to disassemble and assemble the unit.
- Screws that attach the exterior case to the unit should be captive to ensure the test set is assembled securely after the repair activity is completed. This prevents the screws from being lost, the unit is properly attached, and the screws do not get lodged in the unit.
- Use common components, modules, and power supplies whenever possible. This enables interchangeability among product lines and thereby reduces inventory costs and the overall knowledge needed to troubleshoot boards.
- To aid the technician (and manufacturing) in assembly and disassembly, all assemblies and the main unit should be color coded. This will enable quick and easy positioning of assemblies relative to each other and relative to the main unit structure.

To help measure the effectiveness of the above requirements, the *assembly and disassembly cost index* is used. The index is a ratio of the labor cost of disassembly and assembly of the entire unit (number of labor hours multiplied by the standard fully burdened labor rate) *to* the total unit cost (materials, labor, and overhead). This index should not exceed 0.05.

3.2.1.2.2.3 Serviceability. As discussed in the previous section, assembly and disassembly are key determinants of serviceability. Additionally, accessibility is a primary factor to ease serviceability. It is also important for easing assembly using autoinsertion and robotic equipment. Because the effect of accessibility is more than the effect on assembly, it is discussed as part of serviceability. In the assembly process a standard procedure could be used to stack assemblies on top of each other and a "good" assembly process would result. This is not necessarily the case for serviceability. The first assembly in the previous example would be difficult to access, severely affecting the efficiency of the serviceability.

Accessibility concerns include:

- Most units have several board assemblies and subassemblies. It is imperative that these boards be individually accessible so they can be removed to conduct a repair. In other words, the repair technician should not have to remove one or more assemblies which are not being repaired or replaced to gain access to the assembly which is being repaired or replaced.
- Additionally, both the component and solder sides of every PC board should be accessible in the modular block. This enables a minimum amount of movement to position the unit to access a particular assembly or component.

To assess accessibility, an *accessibility index* which is a ratio of the number of accessible board assemblies and major components divided *by* the total number of all board assemblies and major components needs to be determined. The higher the index the better. The 80-20 rule would be a good point to start. This means that 80 percent of the components and assemblies are accessible. If the assembly is not accessible for repair, it must be accessible for testing (test points must be provided for troubleshooting operations). For the purposes of the index calculation, a component or assembly that can be accessed for removal without moving other components has an index of 1.0; if only test points are accessible, the component or assembly has an index of 0.5; and if the component or assembly cannot be accessed to be either removed or tested, the component or assembly has an index of 0.0.

3.2.1.2.2.4 Balancing manufacturability, assembly and serviceability. If all the constraints (including component and assembly alternatives, manufacturability, and serviceability) are to be evaluated, a multidisciplined team should be used. How can alternatives and constraints be considered without mechanical, electrical, and software engineers working together? They cannot!! However, in the past these personnel have not worked together. The result has been higher development, manufacturing, and service costs. Additionally, competitiveness has suffered.

Several methods exist for these personnel to work together to make the trade-offs: sequentially or simultaneously. Literature is very poignant here; these engineers must work together simultaneously. The mechatronics process leverages the simultaneous engineering method to get the diverse engineering groups to work together. This parallel effort is needed throughout the product life cycle, from development to manufacturing and service. Therefore, mechanical, electrical, and software engineers must work together from original concept through product introduction considering each other's constraints as well as manufacturing and serviceability constraints.

Let's take an example to illustrate balancing manufacturability, assembly and serviceability. Assume marketing specifies that an instrument has to fit in a technician's hand because it will be used in the field moving from location to location. Further, the instrument must be able to measure 10 different criteria from easy to complex measurements. Last, the product must be manufactured for a certain cost and the product must be easy to service where the cost of service must not exceed $100.

We know that we are bounded by size. The functionality that is needed will require high-density packaging of electronic componentry to yield the required functionality in the desired package size. Trade-offs need to be made to keep the size as defined yet provide functionality that is cost-effective and easy to assemble and service. Some alternatives include:

- Combine required functionality and manufacture a more complex circuit board.

  Advantages: Reduce the space needed for functionality; possibly lower net cost for the combined final product; more space available to access boards for assembly and service; fewer interconnects.

  Disadvantages: Printed circuit board is more complex and more expensive. The board is most likely to be more complex to service since it is denser (although it may be more accessible).

- Increase the size of the package to house all functionality.

  Advantage: Components are most likely easier to access for manufacturing and service. Electronic componentry is less complex.

  Disadvantage: Acceptability by the marketplace is probably reduced since the required size will not be met.

- Maintain the prescribed package size and reduce the functionality to 8 functions versus 10.

  Advantage: Fewer interconnects; remains a hand-held instrument. Less costly to produce and service.

  Disadvantage: Acceptability of marketplace, since 10 functions required. How does an organization evaluate these alternatives? It is very difficult, if not impossible, if the entire instrument is not considered as an integrated system of interrelated components and assemblies.

The two groups which have to take the primary leadership roles are the electrical and mechanical engineers. Hence a mechatronic view is required to quickly evaluate and select the best alternative. These groups need to work in unison, not sequentially. Otherwise, the most optimum solution is at risk of not being selected. Engineers from Philips Consumer Electronics Division need to make this type of trade-off on a daily basis. They must contend with sophisticated electronic components and circuit boards and ensure that these components and assemblies can be packaged in a plastic or metal housing and be economically manufactured.[4]

When a system view is used and all the disciplines, especially electrical and mechanical engineering, manufacturing, and service, are involved early and simultaneously in the development cycle at the technical feasibility stage, the effort to reach a balance can be minimized, and therefore an optimum product can be developed, manufactured, and serviced. Furthermore, the cost to make modifications is minimized. Therefore, the focus on determining alternatives and conducting trade-off analysis during the technical feasibility or concept stage is optimum. There are software tools that can facilitate the trade-off analysis. These tools are addressed separately later.

3.2.1.3 Development stage. The next and most intensive stage of the development cycle is the actual product development, where the specific components that were identified and confirmed during the technical feasibility stage are designed, in preliminary and final detail. In this stage, size of the target market is finalized, component and assembly drawings are created, prototypes are prepared, the manufacturing and assembly process is finalized, and the product is readied for launch.

The team needs to be of various disciplines to identify and evaluate alternative designs and ultimately finalize the design. A method to help evaluate the alternatives will have significant effect on the final outcome. The more alternatives that can be effectively evaluated the better the final design is likely to be.

A process known as FTA (fault tree analysis) is particularly useful early in this stage. The FTA was developed nearly 30 years ago by Bell Telephone Laboratories. It was developed to assess and improve the reliability of the Minuteman Missile Launch Control System. Using fault tree analysis several weak points in the project were eliminated. Its use was considered successful.

During the sixties and seventies many companies, including Boeing, started to use the technique to improve product reliability. It is especially useful when complex electronic systems are being evaluated

The strength of the FTA approach is that all functional groups have input into engineering, manufacturing, and service. It provides a common medium to study the reasons for failure from an engineering, manufacturing, or service perspective, and make the appropriate corrections. It is useful to prepare this after the trade-off analysis has been performed in the previous stage.

To help understand how this technique is used, the procedure is reviewed and an example discussed.

3.2.1.3.1 FTA procedure[5]

1. Identify top events: use market information, brainstorming, test results, similarity, industry information, etc. "What function must fail to cause the undesirable event to occur?"
2. Pick top events: can develop sequentially or in parallel.
3. List direct, immediate, and sufficient cause(s): preclude "jumping" the deductive chain.
4. Continue "immediate cause" approach for all branches until:
   - Root cause identified
   - Reach point of diminishing return
   - Occurrence of an undeveloped event
5. Evaluate the fault tree
   - Qualitatively—identify common mode failures
   - Quantitatively—numerical probability calculations
6. Recommend and implement corrective action: e.g., redesign, component selection, procurement criteria, maintenance procedures.

Failures can be broken down into three classes according to their causes:

Primary failures

Secondary failures

Command failures

This classification is very useful when constructing the fault tree, as shown in Fig. 3.3.

The analysis of event causes is continued until "basic events" are identified. Therefore, these events should be carefully defined since they mark the limits of the analysis. Note that this analysis of the causes of an undesirable event comes within the scope of the definition of a system (and its components), its boundaries, and its environment.

The basic events in the tree are as follows:

1. The elementary event which need not be further developed (symbol: circle). This event is usually sufficiently well described and

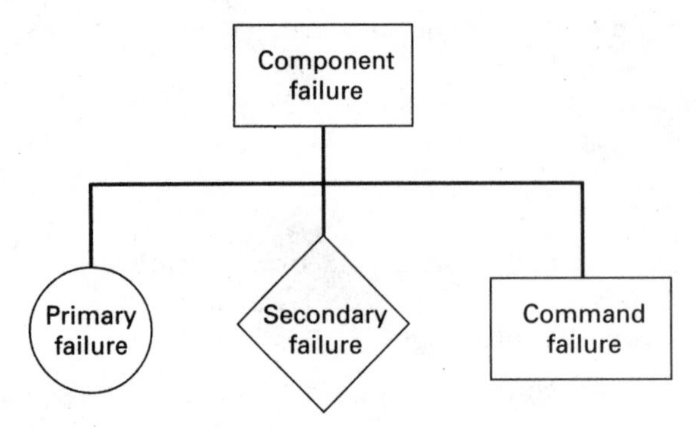

Figure 3.3 Fault tree.

known so that it is useless to determine its causes. Its probability is also known.

2. The event cannot be considered elementary but its causes are not and will not be developed (symbol: diamond). In this case, the boundaries of the system studied are reached when this event is identified.
3. The event cannot be regarded as elementary and its causes are not yet developed, but they will be so later (symbol: double diamond). Analysts consider, then, that they have temporarily reached a boundary in the study and that, as they lack adequate data, the causes of this event will be sought later.
4. The event is one that normally occurs during system operation (symbol: house). This event can be related to the system environment.

3.2.1.3.2 FTA example. The circuit shown in Fig. 3.4 will be used as the case for performing a fault tree analysis. The objective is to present an example to help understand how to construct a FTA. The actual fault tree analysis is presented after the circuit in Fig. 3.5.

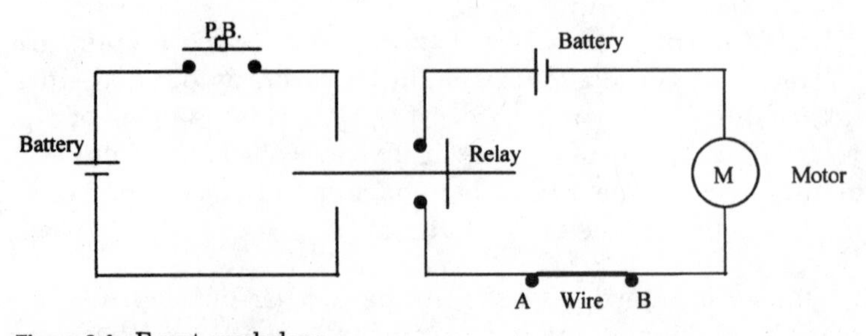

Figure 3.4 Event symbology.

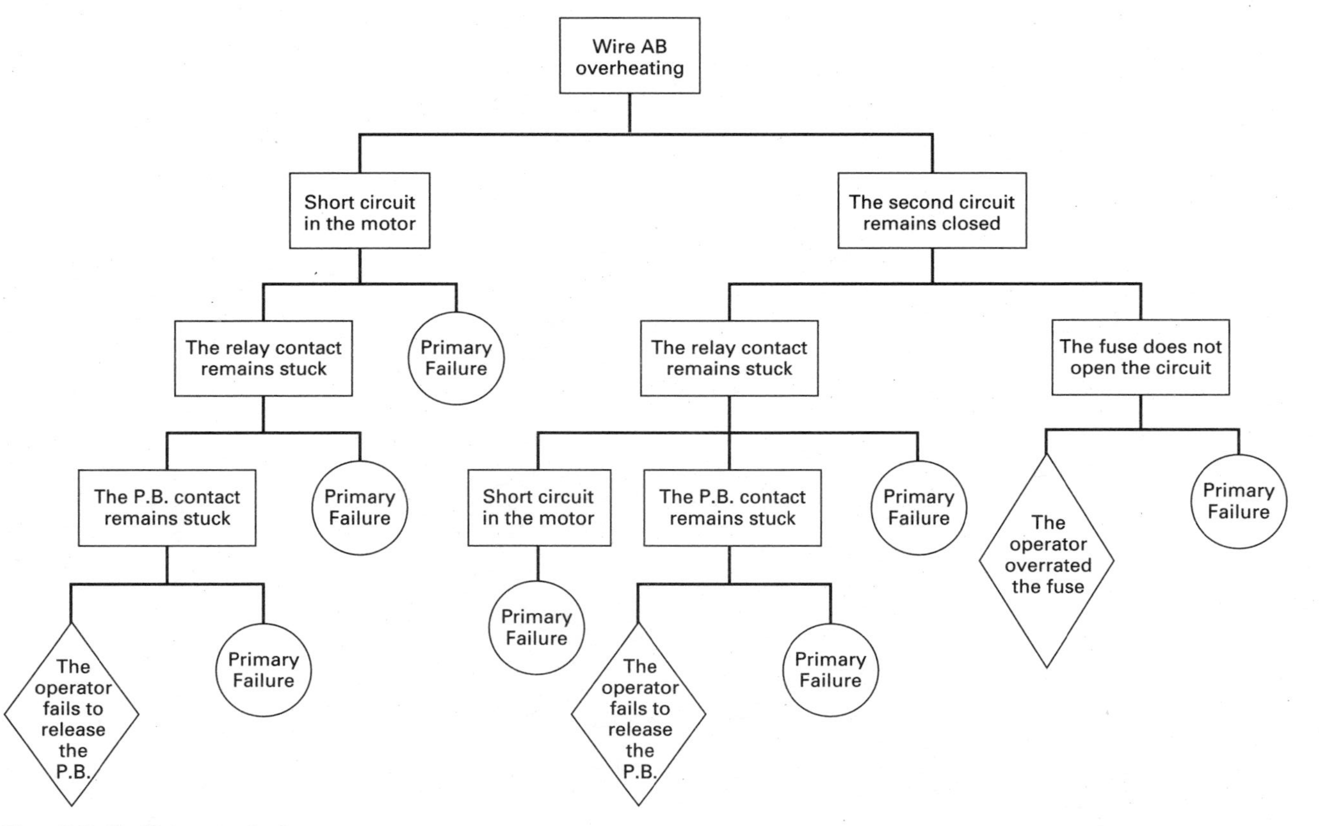

Figure 3.5 Fault tree analysis.

3.2.1.3.3 Conclusion. If all these important steps are first done for electrical components and assemblies, then for mechanical components and assemblies, and finally for software capabilities, this stage can be long and costly. Chances are quite high that any ability to launch the product on-time or in a reduced time frame will be lost, given this sequential mentality. These important steps must be considered using a mechatronic approach. Electrical, mechanical, and software engineers need to work in a cooperative environment looking at the consequences of their joint decision making on the entire product, rather than just the components and assemblies. If only components and assemblies are considered, the team risks optimizing the components and assemblies at the risk of optimizing the entire product. Obviously, in this scenario, the product competitiveness is compromised.

Changes or modifications at this stage are generally quite expensive, but not as prohibitive as costs to modify associated with pilot product or, worse, production or after production delivery to the customer base. So any last minute changes need to occur no later than at this stage. Software tools that can assist the development are addressed in a later section (see Chapter 6).

3.2.1.4 Pilot production. At this stage, the team determines if designing it right the first time is reality or a myth. All the production tooling is in place, actual components and assemblies are received from suppliers, and production at a low volume is performed. Typically in the past, this is where mechanical, electrical, and software engineers considered each other's constraints because pilot production was a disaster. They were not knowledgeable of each other until they were forced into hyperactive mode to solve the set of problems that were identified as a result of pilot production.

In contrast, under the new approach (a mechatronic process) the pilot production stage becomes merely a final verification that the assumptions made by the team's considering each other's constraints and constraints associated with the product life cycle are confirmed. Hence, very few changes result. This is important since changes and modifications required here are extremely prohibitive. If the team has worked together, the changes that may be required will be few and, in most cases, minor. All this leads to a relatively short pilot production phase, paramount to a timely product development cycle.

The activity of mechanical, electrical, and software engineers is significantly reduced because if they have understood each other's constraints through the early stages, problems should be minimal. For those problems that do arise, the team should be able to handle them quickly and easily. In fact, by this time in the development cycle and assuming a mechatronic process, the team has worked closely together for quite some time. Each team should understand the needs and responsibilities of each of the other team members. Hence, because the type of problems that may arise using a mechatronic process should be less complex, the entire team probably will not be needed. One of the team members should be able to solve the problem. As a result, members of the team can be assigned to new projects with one member appointed the point person to handle problems during the pilot production phase.

3.2.1.5 Production. At this stage, suppliers manufacture components and assemblies, and the manufacturer assembles components and assemblies to produce the end product, tests the product for proper performance, and delivers the product to the customer.

During this stage, the development team is disbanded and individuals move on to other projects, unless of course major problems occur. In this case, the team will need to determine solutions to identified problems. The team should include mechanical, electrical, and software engineers. In general, the product design is maintained by a product engineer to correct minor design problems via introducing and implementing ECNs (engineering change notices).

3.2.1.6 Product support. A major determinant of customer satisfaction or customer preference is service or support after the sale. If the manufacturer wants to consider service until this stage, the cost to service and support the product will be extremely high. These expenses can be avoided. The success of this goal is largely determined by serviceability and maintainability constraints considered much earlier in the development cycle.

Upon delivery to the customer, the product must be supported and serviced after the sale. Another group, usually a service department, is responsible for this activity. The original development team is not recognizable. The service group must interact with engineering, usually a product engineer, to provide feedback of pertinent information regarding product performance, quality, and reliability. Minor changes may be required, and in that event, an ECN may be issued and implemented.

References

1. Rovetta, Alberto: "A New Technology with an Old Face and a Proud Heritage," *Mechatronics,* vol. 1, no. 2, 1991.
2. Atkinson and Glasscook: "An Implementation of a Product Data Management System," *Proceedings of the ASME International Computers in Engineering,* August 1990, p. 37.
3. Shina, Sammy: "New Rules for World-Class Companies," *IEEE Spectrum,* July 1991, p. 24.
4. Computervision: "Simultaneous Engineering as a Competitive Advantage," *Computer Aided Engineering,* October 1990, p. C3.
5. Villemeur, Allain: *Reliability, Availability, Maintainability and Safety Assessment,* vol. 1, Wiley, New York, 1992, p. 114.

Part

2

Achieving Mechatronics

Chapter

4

Organizational Structure

This section discusses one of the most important aspects of mechatronics—the people who are involved in using mechatronics to design products. A combination of people working together with the correct set of tools can really bring a mechatronic approach to product design. Even in the absence of elaborate CAD tools mechanical and electrical engineers can collaborate in the product design process. Conversely, a room filled with state-of-the-art CAD tools will never be used to full potential if the engineers won't talk and work with each other. It is the people and organization that form the heart of mechatronics.

Three primary people factors contribute to the successful implementation of a mechatronic methodology. They are:

Management support. Management must be behind the effort and support it on a day-to-day basis. Without this support the collaboration behind mechatronics will die after a few projects.

Teamwork. Mechatronics requires teamwork. For many engineers teamwork is not intuitive but a skill in itself that must be learned.

Product, not mechatronics, focus. A company should focus primarily on its core business, and only then on a particular methodology to support that business. Successful use of mechatronics results from mechanical and electrical engineers working as a team on a project specific to the company's core product or business. If the product is a success, the collaboration between the mechanical and electronics engineers can also be called a success.

To put the people issues in perspective and develop a set of clear recommendations, this section looks at the roles first of the upper and middle manager, and then of the individual contributor. It discusses some of the problems each of these groups face and recommendations as to how they can proceed. (This discussion is approached in a top-down fashion to make it easier to follow and does not suggest the relative importance of the role of each group.)

The section goes on to discuss some general empowerment techniques such as short-term wins, project selection, and enabling change. People at all levels in the organization should be aware of the issues so that they can give feedback if they see that they aren't being addressed.

The section concludes with a brief discussion of matrix versus functional organizational models, and how each of these contributes or distracts from a company's ability to build products with mechatronic design teams.

Before proceeding, it is important to be aware that mechatronics, like its parent methodology concurrent engineering, is not easy to achieve. This is evident from the number of books on the topic of concurrent engineering[1–3] that have specific sections devoted to the organizational issues surrounding its success. Many companies have embarked on a concurrent engineering program only to find their development teams frustrated by the process.

The study results[4] summarized in Table 4.1 show that the vast majority of projects that include interdepartmental collaboration don't succeed. The projects with interdepartmental collaboration tend to develop a great deal of disharmony. This is not to say that there is a strict cause-and-effect relationship between interdepartmental collaboration and project failure. However, it is very important for a company to understand that such collaborations may not succeed and how to prevent failures.

4.1. People and Teams in the Organization

4.1.1 Role of teamwork

We have been so exposed to the glories of working as a team that it might seem natural to have all mechanical and electrial engineers working this way. In reality teams aren't always the best choice for a project organization. Even if a team orientation is appropriate, we

TABLE 4.1

States	Success	Partial success	Failure
Harmony	52	35	13
Mild disharmony	32	45	23
Severe disharmony	11	21	66
Totals	100%	100%	100%

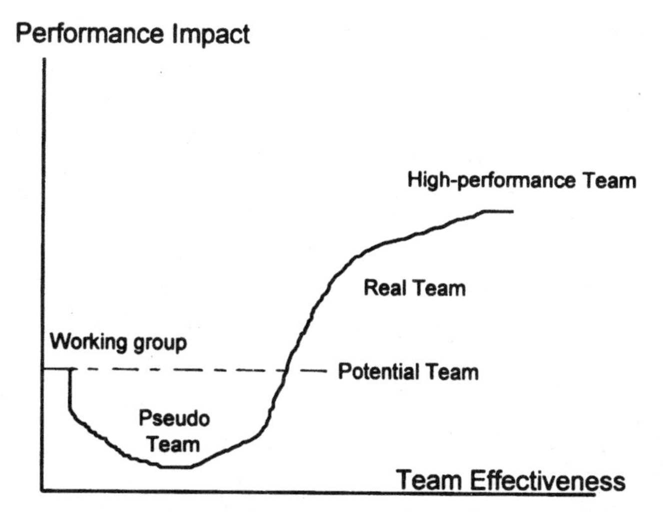

Figure 4.1 Team effectiveness curve.

cannot assume that people on the team have the appropriate skills to start working as a team. Engineers, especially American engineers with their propensity for individualism, do not always fall right into the team model.

4.1.1.1 Are teams always appropriate? Teams are almost always more effective than individuals. Anyone who generally believes in the power of teams tends to think that. However, teams are not always more effective than work groups. Katzenbach and Smith[5] recently described the "team effectiveness" curve shown in Fig. 4.1. In it they show that a work group, or a group of people brought together for a common purpose but acting individually, can actually achieve a greater performance impact than a team transitioning from a work group into a real team.

The two sides of the performance impact valley are occupied by groups of people who share a common purpose and mission. On the left side are work groups. Work groups have a clear purpose and objectives. However, these objectives are accomplished by each member of the group working individually toward individual goals. Group members help each other, but they're measured only on their own individual performance.

The other side of the valley is comprised of teams. Teams also share a clear purpose and objective. The major difference is that the whole team is held mutually accountable for the team's ability to meet its objectives. In this environment one team member's inability to perform a certain task becomes an issue for the team to resolve. In the work group situation the failure would be individual and not an issue for the whole team.

The team approach, as can be seen from Fig. 4.1, has the potential to vastly outperform the work group. However, there is a price. Individuals must, in some sense, forsake some of their individuality to work toward a common goal. They must also devote more time and energy to solving team problems in team discussions. Problems are no longer left to the individual in charge of function X.

If a project can be accomplished by a work group, it might not be appropriate to go through the extra effort to turn the group into a high-performance team. The path between the two can lead to a group that is performing less effectively than a work group or an established team. If a project can be accomplished with many people working as individuals, it may be best to create a work group. For example, a group of 12 mechanical engineers may be assigned to a work group that designs components of a product. Each engineer receives an assignment, carries it through to completion, and then goes on to the next assignment. As long as the designs are completed, the engineer has little need to interact with other mechanical engineers.

If this same group decides that they want to increase the group's throughput by reusing design material, they should become a team. The group has now been given a collective goal which will require that all people work together to help solve.

4.1.1.2 Size. Typically teams will have from 4 to 7 people, but no more than 25. The reason for this is that the greatest performance impact of the team results from optimal communication between team members, which generally happens on smaller teams. As the number of people on the team goes up, the number of potential people to communicate with goes up as 2^n. Therefore, a group of 4 people could have 16 possible communications (manageable), but a group of 10 people can have over 1000 pairwise communications (increasingly unmanageable).

4.1.1.3 Purpose. Clarity of purpose is one of the most important requirements for a team. Without a clear purpose each member can attempt to do different things. At times these actions will be diametrically opposed. When people on a team work in opposite directions, the total effective team output is actually less than the sum of individual outputs.

A clearly stated purpose can be used to align all the efforts of the team. This common direction will help individual efforts complement each other rather than cancel each other out.

4.1.1.4 Skills. The basic definition of a team is a group of people that bring together a diverse set of complementary skills. A mechatronics team obviously should have people with a background in electrical and mechanical engineering. These electrical and mechanical skills are technical skills. A list of some of the specific skills that may be required on the team can be determined by reviewing the course listing in the educational section.

The team will also need the necessary people skills to build the team. The goal is to create a team with a diverse set of people skills such that the team will succeed. For example, if the team was built only of "dreamers," it would be very difficult for it to produce specific results. Common available surveys, such as the Beldin survey, measure a team's "people" skills. Such a survey can be used to determine if the team is comprised of all one type of individual, and if so what are some of the other skills that the team may want to build on.

4.1.1.5 Team leader. The team leader is the person responsible for defining the purpose and goals of the group which provide a sense of direction. It is the team leader's responsibility to ensure that everyone understands this direction.

Aside from keeping the group generally on track, the team leader role does not have to stay with one person. This role can switch from person to person depending on the skills required. If the team is trying to solve a problem with a strong mechanisms orientation, the person with the strongest mechanisms background may step in to give the team direction.

A good team leader will know when to focus on team goals and when to step back, allowing someone else to lead a particular problem-solving effort.

4.1.1.6 Team phases. Teams go through three clear phases during the life cycle of a project—introductions, contributions, and breakup. These phases are necessary phases which take place in every group. Unless everyone on a new team has worked together before on a previous team, it is likely that each phase will take more than one meeting or one day.

When the team is initially formed, it goes through a phase of general introductions in which team members explore the backgrounds of their fellow team members. This getting-to-know-one-another phase is more than just passing around résumés to understand technical abilities. Many different nontechnical skills such as interpersonal or writing skills will be valuable to the team at different points in time.

Once people know one another, team members try to find roles for themselves based on their abilities and the team goals. A team leader who is strong and familiar with individuals may assign these roles based on an understanding of people's backgrounds.

The process of getting to know one another can be facilitated by a kickoff meeting with general introductions. Typically one meeting won't suffice. Additional skills will surface as these skills are needed by the team. One way to help to learn about each other's skills is to actually work on a miniproject as a kickoff activity for the team. This can be an activity that also accomplishes the team goal or an outing to an obstacle course where the goal is for all team members to complete the course, with the assistance of other team members.

In other cases the team leader may decide to let the team go through several meetings before defining specific team roles. This allows the team leader to observe each individual within the context of the team before assigning specific roles. The Japanese typically give a new employee in a company a 6- to 12-month period in which to just "get a sense of the organization" before starting to make a specific contribution. From a team point of view this 6- to 12-month period allows the individual and other members of the team to really understand each other and how the individual will contribute to the team. This period also allows management to understand individual employees, their backgrounds, and how they interact with other people before making a specific job assignment.

Once people have settled into specific roles, each member is ready to contribute to the team goals. This phase of the team can last for several months until the team is ready to break up. This is the most productive time period for the team. It is during this time that team members are using their knowledge about each other to ensure that the strengths of each person are employed to their fullest.

During the contribution phase team members will also need to use other skills such as negotiation to ensure that progress is continually made toward the team's objectives.

At the team breakup everyone should be thanked for their contribution. The team leader may want to make this a special occasion, and even invite management from outside the team to attend a breakup ceremony at which team members can be acknowledged for the work they've done. The team breakup stage is also the time to measure the team's performance so that other teams can benefit from the historical data.

4.1.1.7 Measuring whether you are really a team. If you've ever been on a team or are considering starting a team, it might be interesting to use the following checklist to determine if your group is really behaving like a team, or merely a work group of individuals.

- Do members of the group refrain from blaming others in the group for problems?
- Do members readily help each other with problems?
- Is there an open exchange of ideas at meetings?
- Does the leadership role move about based on people's particular areas of expertise?
- Do people freely get together to exchange ideas?
- Are issues fully discussed at team meetings (or is there more discussion after a meeting than during the meeting)?

If the answer to any of these questions is no, the so-called team has some characteristics of a work group. If the answers to all of the above questions are no, the group is definitely a work group, not a team.

4.1.2 Conflict resolution

4.1.2.1 Is conflict okay? Yes. In fact it is normal when a team of people from different backgrounds come together. It is also bound to happen when the team includes highly skilled members who take pride in their contributions. They may not want to back down from a position, especially if it compromises their stance within the team.

The key is to have a process in place to manage these conflicts and achieve resolutions, keeping the team intact, ready to face the next problem or conflict.

4.1.2.2 Negotiation. Whenever people are working together on a team, there are bound to be differences of opinion. In some cases these opinions can't be reconciled without some form of negotiation. This negotiation can be on items as simple as estimating project schedules, or on much more complex topics such as whether to use air suction or conveyor belts in a part transfer mechanism.

Whenever a team is built from people with diverse engineering backgrounds who don't necessarily understand the other disciplines there is an even greater need to understand the basics of negotiation.

Several books have been written on the topic; therefore, this section focuses only on some points that are especially relevant to a diverse team of engineers.

One of the most important points in negotiation is to understand the other party's interest.[6] For two engineers on opposite sides of the table to completely understand each other's interests, they may both require several years of graduate school. However, every effort should be made. For example, a mechanical engineer may say that it is impossible to achieve the product's required cycle time since it is impossible to decelerate a particular mechanism because of inertia. At this point the negotiation has come to a standstill. The electrical engineer could take the lead and ask why this can't be done. Do all the linkages have to have so much mass? What is the trade-off between a lighter metal in the linkages versus a stronger motor that could handle the deceleration?

Communication skill is another important factor to consider when engineers negotiate. Progress can't be made if the engineers do not communicate their ideas. This communication process can happen at two levels. At the first level is the openness to listening to other opinions that the engineer expresses through both body language and speech. If the engineer isn't communicating or is hostile to the concept of new ideas, meaningful communication is unlikely. The second level is to actually communicate the ideas. Some engineers have great ideas but are unable to communicate them in a meaningful way.

Focusing on problems instead of people is the final and most valuable lesson that people involved with mechatronics should learn. It is very easy to attack other people's "stupidity" if they do not immediately understand the reasons for a particular decision. However, such an attack will only divert their attention from the problem to their own wounded ego. It is much more important for engineers to look at the common problem they are trying to solve. They must weigh the merits of each proposal based on the goals of the project, not on the egos of the individuals involved in the discussion.

4.1.3 Role of upper management

Upper management support is critical in any effort that requires coordination between different engineering disciplines. According to the TQM guru Dr. Deming, the burden for implementing a quality program (or in the case of this book a mechatronic program) rests squarely on the shoulders of upper management. Upper management in this case is the lowest level in the management hierarchy where the electronics, mechanical, software, and control engineering departments converge. Typically this person will be the vice president or director of engineering (see Fig. 4.2).

4.1.3.1 Sponsorship. Possibly the most important role of upper management is to sponsor the use of mechatronics as a methodology to achieve better products that are developed as quickly and reliably as possible. Without this high-level support it is doubtful that the collab-

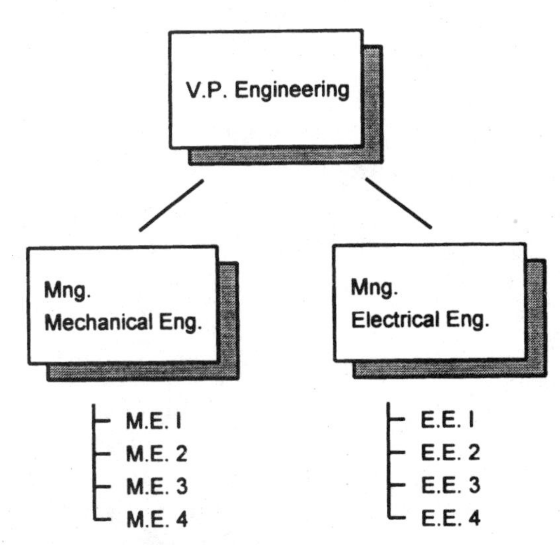

Figure 4.2 Management hierarchy.

oration required to achieve mechatronics will live beyond the first one or two projects. Upper management's support is essential to counteract the territorialism that may develop from within the specific engineering departments. Upper management's support comes by helping to select a project that can succeed, protecting the project that is trying to use mechatronics for the first time, setting an example as to the behavior middle management should be using, and sending the correct message to middle management to encourage them to also support a project's use of mechatronics.

4.1.3.2 Choosing the project. Upper management should have a large role in selecting the mechatronics team's project. Upper management has a good idea of how much visibility each project will have. It also can determine whether schedule or cost goals might become so dominant that they force team participants to fall back into their standard modes of operation because they know that they have worked in the past. [Guidelines for this selection are discussed later in this chapter.]

4.1.3.3 Protector. Upper management can serve in the critical role of protector. In this role the upper manager gives a newly formed team of mechanical and electrical engineers the time and space they need to establish some early project wins. Without this protection team members might be forced back into their old ways of doing things by any number of political or external factors.

The protector role of upper manager can help in two areas. First, it can help to staff the team sufficiently so that participants won't feel overwhelmed by the added responsibility. Second, once the team is established and working, the upper manager can protect the team from being robbed of resources or distracted by other activities in the organization. If the upper manager helps in both areas, the team will have a much greater chance of success.

4.1.3.4 Example setting. Middle management and individual workers listen to what upper management says but also watch the day-to-day behavior of the upper manager. Therefore, it is critical that behavior of the upper manager reinforces the words spoken at large meetings and in policy statements.

If the upper manager selects a pilot project and allows a team to be formed to work on the project but then makes day-to-day decisions that don't support the team goals, the team will probably fail. For example, after a project has been selected, upper management could make budget decisions that prevent the team from having the necessary hardware and software tools needed to get the job done.

4.1.3.5 Sending the proper message to middle management. Middle management will probably feel threatened by the collaboration required for mechatronics to succeed. Instead of electrical decisions that affect mechanical engineering having to trickle up through the electrical manager, across to the mechanical manager, and down to the individual mechanical engineers, the individual contributors work together directly. This may lead middle managers to question their own contributions to the organization.

It is imperative that upper management be sensitive to the middle managers' issues. One company approached this problem by first announcing that upper management wanted to improve the collaboration between two departments by sitting down and reorganizing the work flows of the two departments. In the same breath it announced that all middle managers would be guaranteed a job after the reorganization. This level of commitment allowed middle managers to step back freely and help the upper manager solve what was now viewed to be a nonthreatening common problem.

4.1.3.6 Establishing rewards to entice individuals to change. Upper management can go a long way in motivating change by establishing rewards for those that do change. For example, employee reviews can include sections that measure the level of cooperation the employee exhibits with other departments. Or upper management can ensure that a pilot team or individual team members are recognized in a public way. A team can be recognized for innovative engineering, making a tight product schedule, or exemplary team behavior. Individual team members can be rewarded for team commitment and openness to the other disciplines involved. This recognition can be as simple as an employee of the month award given to, for example, a mechanical engineer who comes up with the best electrical innovation on a product (alone or with an electrical engineer).

4.1.4 Role of middle management

The middle manager can be the most threatened by the formation of mechatronic design teams. This is especially true of middle managers previously involved in a functionally aligned organization. As individuals in the department disperse to separate teams, managers may feel they're losing control of the organization. They may even find that their staff sits in other offices or "team" areas more frequently than in the department. Managers accustomed to measuring their power strictly by the number of people who must come to them for final approval on decisions will feel frustrated with the new cross-functional teams.

This chapter goes on to examine "power" in more detail. However, the word power is not used in a derogatory sense. It is used in much more of an engineering sense as the ability to get things done. Middle management typically relied on getting things done because people who reported directly were required to do whatever the manager said if they wanted the reward of raises or esteem.

One way to look at how the new middle manager might retain a sense of job satisfaction is to look at the nature of power. Power can come from several different areas. Traditionally middle managers have power because the company has declared that certain people report to them. These managers are responsible for these employees' reviews, defining their projects, etc. Power is granted by the organization.

An environment in which mechatronics can succeed much more frequently requires a team approach. People move on and off teams, and the team leader may make more day-to-day assignments than the department manager. The authority granted by the organization that used to give the middle manager a sense of power has been taken away.

4.1.4.1 Knowledge. However, the middle manager, as Fig. 4.3 shows, still has two other ways to achieve power. Both of these, knowledge and coalitions, can actually give more power than the authority granted by the company.

Middle managers can continue to have power by becoming experts in a particular area. They might choose to become a resource for local university programs that would enable their employees to become cross-trained.

For example, the middle manager could encourage members of the department to take courses in disciplines of other departments. In

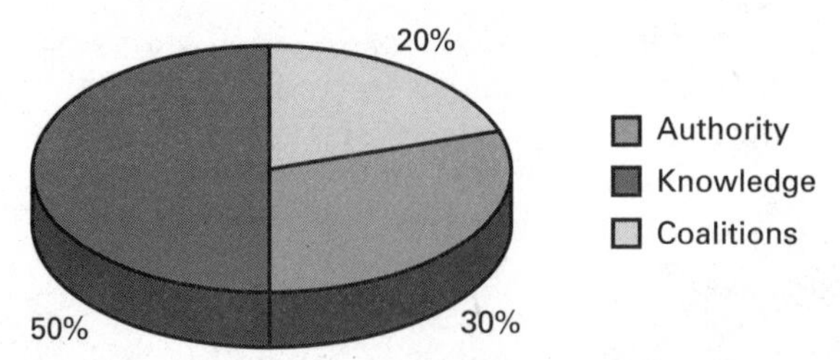

Figure 4.3 Two ways that middle managers achieve power.

contrast to this, a particular middle manager undermined the efforts of a young mechanical engineer to take courses in assembly language programming by proclaiming, "You'll never need to use that in this department." In effect the manager was trying to keep the departmental walls intact.

4.1.4.2 Coalitions. So what options does the middle manager have in an environment where functional alignment has been the norm? In a sea of change the middle manager has the potential to really inspire a team. Probably the most important way for the middle manager to perform in this role is to become an enabler and advocate for change.

The middle manager can lead by way of example. The manager of an electrical engineering department could volunteer to work on a product troubleshooting team with the manager of the mechanical engineering department. Such an arrangement has positive benefits above and beyond the signal it sends to the employees by starting to ease the managers into a more technical role. In this way the managers start to see that there are more ways to contribute in the "new" organization than directly coordinating the day-to-day activities of a group. In many instances middle managers enjoy assuming more technical responsibility and getting away from some of the politics and paper pushing that sometimes consume their time.

Another key area of contribution for the middle manager is team building. As cross-functional teams are brought together, a manager who thwarts these efforts will undermine the teams' abilities to succeed and be viewed as negative influence. Or a manager could help the company and the team succeed by sponsoring team-building activities. Middle managers can receive recognition on two fronts: first, by encouraging the mechatronic design teams they gain positive visibility with upper management; and second, actively training people in team participation helps them retain their power as experts in team building.

4.1.5 Role of the individual

It is very easy to place full responsibility for the success of a project with middle and upper management and ignore the individual's responsibilities. However, as we will see in Sec. 4.2.3, in many cases a small group of individuals can actually train upper management in the benefits of a mechatronic methodology.

One of the biggest issues is for workers to look past how a change in their daily practices will affect their relationship with the department next door, and focus on how these changes will affect the company's competitive relationship with the company next door. A mechanical engineer may find it very disconcerting for an electrical engineer to make recommendations about how a particular mechanism should be designed. However if, as a result, the team comes up with a better, more competitive product, it doesn't mater whether the recommendation came from an electrical or mechanical engineer.

In many cases innovative team recommendations enable some companies to move ahead while others slowly decay. In today's market one cannot sit around and rely on methodologies of the past. Competition is coming from all over the world, including eager young companies based in third world countries that don't have the historical departmental walls.

4.1.6 Matrix organizations vs. functional organizations

In the matrix organization individuals report to both a specific project and into a functional organization. Individuals are rotated from project to project as the need for their specific functional disciplines arises. Chrysler has such an organizational structure. The projects in this case are car platforms such as luxury vehicles or four-wheel-drive passenger cars. An example of the matrix organization with a few personnel assignments is depicted in Fig. 4.4.

The matrix organization has two subvariants, depending on where the emphasis in the organization is placed. The organization is either strongly focused on function and weakly focused on projects, or strongly focused on projects and weakly focused on function.

A company using mechatronics should build project teams focused on a project. This project focus will allow mechanical and electrical engineers to work cooperatively together without the walls that get built in a functionally oriented organization.

4.1.6.1 Dealing with matrix problems. A major problem facing a project-driven matrix organization is developing continuity and technical innovation within functional areas. There are several ways in which

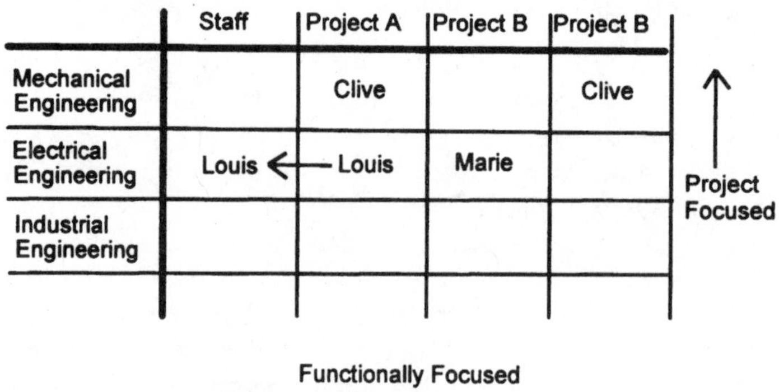

	Staff	Project A	Project B	Project B
Mechanical Engineering		Clive		Clive
Electrical Engineering	Louis ←	Louis	Marie	
Industrial Engineering				

↑ Project Focused

Functionally Focused

Figure 4.4 Matrix organization chart.

companies address this problem. In a very large company there may be a separate functional area that just does research on new technologies. People may be hired specifically into this research area. In smaller companies there may be one or two people doing research permanently assigned to a functional area.

A company can greatly strengthen its functional departments even in a project-focused matrix organization by rotating people from projects into staff positions in the functional disciplines. Periodically putting engineers back into functional organizations allows them to look at several projects at a time and consider how their decisions and actions on one project can be applied to other projects. For example, when Louis is done with his assignment on Project A he would shift back to a staff position in the electrical engineering department. Also, people in the functional organization, though they may not be working on a project at the time, are viewed by the project teams as having a great appreciation for project work. The "project people" versus "research people" wall will thus be broken down.

Another frequent problem in the matrix organization is that individuals have both a functional "manager" and a project team leader. From management's point of view multiple people with different priorities are all contending for the same resource. This problem can be compounded if an individual,such as Clive, is assigned to multiple projects, each with a team leader, and still has a functional manager. One way to resolve this is for upper management to clarify what the priorities of the respective projects are. In this way the resources can be allocated best to meet the company's objectives.

Individuals may feel that their time is being split between too many activities. Again the best way to resolve this is for upper management to clarify the priorities. In this way the individual engineer can focus on one particular project for a greater period of time. The ability to focus will increase the engineer's productivity, which in turn will ease some of the scheduling problems of the project leader.

In mature matrix organizations the functional managers will have already adopted some of the ideas we've suggested for the middle manager. They will not be trying to build a functional wall. Rather they will try to promote the ability of their functional area to meet the objectives of the company through the special knowledge that they have about their functional area.

4.1.7 Mechatronics problems caused by a functional organization

A functionally aligned organization puts the major emphasis on functional areas. Projects pass from functional department to functional department sequentially. Though it is possible to achieve a low level of mechatronics within a functional organization, it should be avoided by any company that seriously wants to pursue mechatronics.

The biggest problem is that functionally aligned groups make decisions that are not based on the best interest of a specific deliverable of the company. Each group will make decisions that are best for its function. For example, a major car manufacturer has a "power train" (engines and transmissions) division responsible for all power trains for all cars. Its former approach to product development was to create a next generation power train, then look for a car body in which to put it. The problem is, what if the next generation power train really doesn't meet the requirements of the customer? Either the power train has to change, or it is not used at all.

When mechanical and electrical engineers from a functionally aligned organization get together, they will have two conflicting goals. One goal is to participate in the design team. The other goal is to further the interests of their particular department, even if these interests don't further the goals of the design team. Imagine the opinions of a hydraulics engineer involved in the design of the mechatronic-based steering system from TRW. In a purely functionally aligned organization the hydraulics engineer might try to sabotage the mechatronics-based steering system.

The main advantage of the functionally aligned organization is that from project to project there is continuity. As the department works on each project it can apply its experience from one project to the next, reducing design costs. The ability to carry forward designs also allows the functional organization to amortize design costs over several projects. This allows the functional organization to take risks larger than those a specific project team would take because the costs can be divided among several projects.

4.2 General Techniques

Now that many of the people issues have been discussed, this section discusses some general techniques to consider when starting a mechatronics-based project. There is no reason to choose a project that might fail owing to reasons outside the control of the design team. Likewise, setting up for successes early in the design cycle empowers and further motivates the team.

4.2.1 Choose a project

Choosing the right project is not a simple task, especially if it is the first step into mechatronic design for a company. A company should consider how well a project correlates to its business objectives, the size of the project, and how technological risks might cause the project to fail.

The importance of selecting a project versus training employees in various empowerment programs was highlighted by a study conducted by the American Electronics Association. In over 300 electronics companies it found that "63% of them had failed to improve quality defects by even as much as 10%"[7] even though they all had a total quality program underway. Targeting a program at a specific area such as quality does not guarantee that quality will get better. Likewise a declaration from upper management that, "we will lower product manufacturing costs through better design tradeoffs between our electrical and mechanical engineers," will not guarantee the reduction of product manufacturing costs. Instead of defining a "program," management needs to pick a project that is critical to the company, and then use the program as one of the ways to achieve this project.

4.2.1.1 Correlation to the company's products. Most companies do not exist to try out a mechatronics product development methodology, TQM, Concurrent Engineering, or other strategy. Most companies exist to make money by selling products or services. To ensure the successful introduction of mechatronics a company should choose a project that relates directly to the end product(s) the company sells. The project could be associated with a product or the manufacturing of a product. The techniques of mechatronics can be used to achieve specific goals such as increased functionality or decreased manufacturing costs on this product or a product manufacturing process.

For example, TRW wanted to develop a new steering system for cars. They required a mechanism that was ecologically friendly, used less power, and was configurable to suit the end needs of different types of cars. The solution was based on a purely mechatronic design that combined the mechanical rack of a typical steering system with a torque sensor, electronic control unit, and a variable-reluctance motor that controlled the rack.

The project team could link the success of the project, including collaboration between the mechanical and electrical engineers, directly to TRW's ability to earn revenue through this new product introduction.

Unless the project is directly linked to a company's product, management can easily dismiss it as not adding value to the business, regardless of whether the project and its use of mechatronics was a success.

The term "product" is chosen specifically over "corporate objective." This is a conscious decision made to avoid falling into a trap. A project selected to meet a corporate objective such as "the use of mechatronics in all product designs" can easily fail in terms of value to the company. As we have seen from the survey of Total Quality Management programs, it is not effective to simply declare a methodology to be an objective unto itself and then develop projects aimed at satisfying that objective.

4.2.1.2 Not too big. It is very important not to choose too large a project, especially for a first project. TRW's steering system design would be too large a project for a company just starting to take advantage of mechatronics. The TRW steering system was developed as part of a 10-year development project.

The first project should be a three- to six-man year project. This will keep both the number of people and the duration of the project to a size that is easy to coordinate and easy to demonstrate clear wins on. The duration of the project should be less then one year. However, it should have demonstrable results within the first month. Quick results will help bolster team confidence and help provide fuel for future successes. The project should have no more then six to ten people. A project with any more people will become too large to control and at the same time ensure success.

4.2.1.3 Minimize technology risk. Using mechatronics to introduce new technology is not a good place to start if the mechanical and electrical engineers are not already working together. The mechatronic design team should start with very simple, readily available technology and focus on working together to produce better designs. Sticking with standard technology will remove one of the risks that could otherwise undermine the initial project's success. As several projects are completed successfully, the design team might consider more technologically advanced areas such as fuzzy logic as a new control scheme.

The project can be as simple as the selection of a fuse holder. For example, a manufacturer of light curtains found that the type of fuse holder they used made it impossible to replace the fuse once the product was installed. The remedy was to select a different fuse holder. This required interaction between the mechanical-industrial engineer that laid out the light curtain, and the electrical engineer that defined the type of fuse holder to use. The project was simple, it required collaboration between the mechanical-industrial engineer and the electrical engineer, and there was a direct benefit to the company in terms of a better product as perceived by the customer.

4.2.2 Look for short-term wins

We continually hear that one of the downfalls of the American business system is its emphasis on short-term returns on investment. Managers are forced to justify capital expenditures based on an increasingly short time frame. On the other hand, the long-term outlook of the Japanese has been seen as a major contributor to the success of Japanese business.

One could argue that if upper management was willing to change its focus to the long term, large organizational and cultural changes such as those required by a mechatronics methodology would have a much better chance of succeeding. The problem is that the people who actually do the work need to be motivated on a daily, weekly, or monthly basis. People need to know that what they are doing is helping the company and is worth the changes and extra effort.

Enabling a team to experience a short-term win empowers the team. Each success reinforces the team's feeling that it is on a successful project. In contrast, a long-drawn-out project with no milestones within the first 6 months can destroy a team.

Furthermore, tying each of these successes to the company's product objectives gives every employee a sense that what is being accomplished is meaningful because it directly benefits the company. Individual milestones can be plotted to show how they are contributing to a larger goal. For example, in a long project like TRW's steering system it is very important to have shorter wins. For the TRW project, these wins came when the customer programming environment for the steering system control system was developed, and when a suitable feedback technology was chosen to give drivers the same feeling in the steering wheel that they had with a hydraulically driven steering system.

Finally there is no reason to be quiet about success. People enjoy receiving a compliment from upper management, especially if it is done in a public setting. Typically employees will receive several follow-up acknowledgments from their peers. These acknowledgments amplify the impact of those given by upper management.

4.2.3 Enablers of change

Certain things make one transition easier than others. Two very clear ways to enable change are to develop a transition plan and to make sure that employees are appropriately educated.

4.2.3.1 Transition plan. The roles of the various people in the organization have been spelled out. It's clear what type of organization should be in place, but what is the first move and who will make it? Should upper management come out with a new slogan? Should upper management develop a sweeping program to educate and train everyone in engineering?

Don Clausing, author of *Total Quality Development,*[8] has some excellent ideas on the roll-out of an improvement plan. He suggests starting in the lower right quadrant shown in Fig. 4.5 with a mechatronics pilot project, chosen according to the guidelines previously outlined, done by a core group.

This core group then becomes the teacher of upper management. The core group can show upper management how mechatronics was used in their project, how the project directly enhanced the company's product, and how it could be used in other projects throughout the organization. As management's understanding grows, they will work with the core group to develop a larger-scale implementation plan.

With the implementation plan in hand upper management is now ready to lead the rest of the organization in using mechatronics. Management can start several more pilot projects with a clear vision of the benefit that they will provide to the company. Management believes that each of these projects should succeed because the kinks have been worked out in the core group's pilot project, and the same problems need not be experienced.

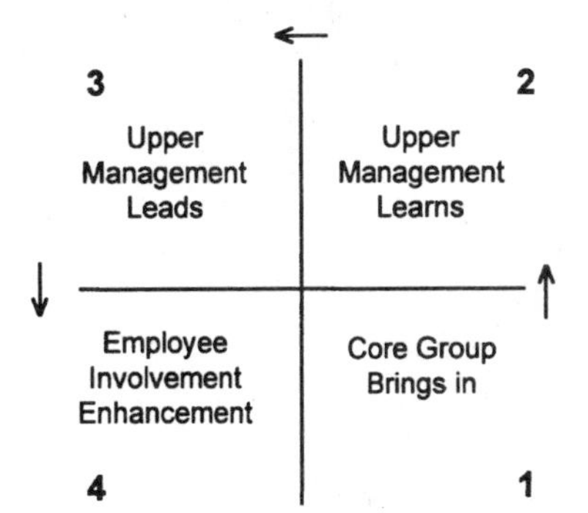

Figure 4.5 A mechatronics pilot project.

Finally, employees throughout the organization are assigned to the projects and start to tailor the methodologies that were piloted in the first project to the individual needs of their team.

In effect this roll-out plan is a detailed summary of the plan-do-check-act cycle that Dr. Deming has advocated for the past 40 years. The core group does some initial planning and doing. The core group checks their work and sells the concept to upper management. Upper management turns around and implements mechatronics throughout the organization.

4.2.3.2 Training. Education is one of the key enablers in a change to mechatronics. Education, as will be emphasized in the next chapter, takes place at several different levels. Some of the areas where engineers can be educated are how to work as a team, how to do top-down or system-level design in order to be aware of the trade-offs being made. At a more discipline-oriented level engineers can broaden their background, getting training in another discipline. For example, a mechanical engineer could take courses in microprocessor programming, or an electrical engineer could take a basic class in mechanical devices.

Mechatronics can be enhanced by receiving training in teamwork or by reading one of the many books on concurrent engineering.

4.2.4 Reasons the mechatronic methodology fails

Common reasons for mechatronics to fail are rooted in the people and process issues. Software and hardware tools are secondary to the people and process issues. Some of the most common reasons for failure are:

- *Lack of upper management support.* Upper management overtly opposes the collaboration between mechanical and electrical engineers. Or upper management endorses the concept but never really uses its energy to support the pilot project, help people's attitudes change by creating the right environment, or provide the appropriate training.
- *Middle management is stronger than upper management.* If middle management has even slightly more power than upper management, departmental issues will be emphasized over cross-departmental issues. Middle management doesn't necessarily have to be strong; they just have to be stronger than upper managment. This strength can be overtly displayed by ignoring what upper management says, or covertly displayed by not aligning day-to-day practices with upper management's objective to foster cross-department cooperation.

- *Initial pilot projects fail.* The failure of an initial pilot project can mean the end of a mechatronic design approach. The reasons for failure may have nothing to do with the team assembled or their spirit of cooperation. Nonetheless, the initial project's failure can still be viewed as proof that mechatronics does not work, and as a reason not to pursue a second mechatronics project. This is why it is so important to choose a project carefully, according to the guidelines presented earlier.
- *Lack of support tools and infrastructure.* For mechatronics to succeed there must be a set of software- and hardware-based tools to enable engineers to readily communicate designs. Without this support cooperation will be much more difficult and engineers might revert to their nonproject modes of thought.

References

1. Kusiak, Andrew: *Concurrent Engineering, Automation, Tools, and Techniques,* Wiley-Interscience, New York, 1992.
2. Parsaei, Hamid (ed.): *Concurrent Engineering, Contemporary Issues and Modern Design Tools,* Chapman & Hall, New York, 1993, part 1.
3. Clausing, Don: *Total Quality Development,* ASME Press, New York, 1994, Chap. 2.
4. Souder, W. E.: *Managing New Product Innovations,* Macmillan, New York, 1986, p. 170.
5. Katzenbach, Jon, and Douglas Smith: *The Wisdom of Teams,* Harper Business, New York, 1993, p. 84.
6. Ury, William and Roger Fisher: *Getting to Yes,* Penguin Books, New York, 1983, p. 41.
7. Schaeffer, Robert and Harvey Thomson: "Successful Change Programs Begin with Results," *Harvard Business Review,* January–February 1992, p. 81.
8. Clausing, Don: *Total Quality Development,* ASME Press, New York, 1994, p. 411.

Chapter

5

Education

> Joe Wujek [former Apple, Inc., engineer] recruited dozens of engineering students [during the 1980s] and didn't like what he saw. Science-heavy studies and narrow specialization had left the new prospects without the skills to design products that mix mechanical and electronic components.[1]

Joe Wujek shares a problem common to many managers in industry. The typical student trained by universities is ill-equipped to tackle mechatronic problems. Because most products today include a mechatronic base, the lack of a trained engineering labor source is an ominous problem for industry. This chapter discusses how people in industry, such as Joe Wujek, and academia can develop mechatronic curricula and company strategies to help fill the training void that exists between industry and academia.

Engineering universities today have ample incentive to make these curriculum changes. From a political point of view they have been hammered by news articles bemoaning the gap between what industry needs and what academia is producing. From a business point of view emphasis on mechatronics as a way to solve industry's problem has sound merit. If industry wants better-trained students, universities that are successful in training them can place a greater number of students in prestigious firms. A higher, more successful placement record in turn attracts more talented students, which bolsters the reputation of the university and its faculty.

This is not to say that there hasn't been progress. The number of universities that offer programs or classes in mechatronics keeps growing every year. A partial list of universities in Japan, the United States, and Europe that offer mechatronic programs is given in Appendix A. In some cases a formal department or professorial chair is devoted to mechatronics. One could easily argue that any university that has a mechanical and electrical engineering department, in effect, offers a program in mechatronics. A list of such universities would cover all the major universities in the world. Rather Appendix A lists universities that have a formal focus on mechatronics. It also includes universities that have a "lab" devoted to mechatronics. This is the typical organization in Japan. A major university such as Tokyo Institute might have a department devoted to mechanical engineering. Within that department will be many labs devoted to particular topics and headed by individual professors. Many labs in Japan are focused on mechatronics. Above and beyond individual university-level focus, consortiums within industry and academia help raise the level of training in mechatronics. Industry leader Motorola Inc. has established "Motorola University" to train students in the application of various IC products in mechatronic problems. The *Mechatronic Journal,* established in 1990, receives and publishes a wide number of mechatronic focused papers from throughout the world. In the United States a group of universities have formed the "Synthesis Coalition" to reach out to minorities and broad age ranges by providing a standard curriculum to the member universities. Stanford University is using the efforts of the "Synthesis Coalition" to expand its mechatronics program into the undergraduate realm.

5.1 Common Problems in Industry and Academia

Despite this progress there is still a lot of work to be done, in both industry and academia. One of the biggest obstacles to progress is organizational structure. Both business and academia tend to be organized around single functions instead of around teams that can solve their organization's needs. Organizations within academia focus very deeply on functional disciplines. There might be an electrical or mechanical engineering department. This department is stratified into undergraduate, graduate, and postgraduate programs. It earns respect by making further advances in the major topic area of the department. For example, if the electrical engineering department can discover the next generation of microwave guides it will receive recognition from competing engineering schools, grants from industry, etc. Given the functional focus of engineering departments it is no wonder that students don't get the opportunity to explore the disciplines of other departments.

The good news is that some universities are starting to combine engineering departments for more effective cross training. In more radical cases people like Joe Wujek have moved to academia to provide this training. Prof. Wujek designed a program that allowed senior students to provide project management of some of the younger students. To facilitate this collaboration a senior level and a freshman class were scheduled together and located in two adjoining rooms. Throughout the semester Prof. Wujek had the younger students do labs that required team leadership from the seniors.

In industry, consider an automotive manufacturer. The electronic design problem initially involved ignition and lighting systems. It could be supported by a relatively small group of people. Then with the advent of more complex door-locking systems, rear-view mirror controls, etc., pockets of electronic design sprouted up within the various design departments at the manufacturer. They realized that all these discrete design teams were being left out of some of the key mechanical decisions taking place in the overall car design. To solve this problem they created a single department responsible for all electronic design within the car. The problem is that this department works as a separate department, instead of a department that must integrate its activities with the rest of the automobile design process. Now the manufacturer is trying to make progress at integrating the efforts of this central electronics department with the rest of the company.

5.2 Mechatronics at the Undergraduate Level

There are those who argue that mechatronics cannot be taught at the undergraduate level. At a pragmatic level this makes immediate sense and explains why industry receives students who are so ill equipped. One can easily argue that in order to be successful in mechatronics students should complete two undergraduate degrees, one in mechanical and the other in electrical engineering. The icing on the cake would be graduate-level work in system design and control theory using the training obtained in both undergraduate degrees.

Students with two degrees would have most of the necessary analytic tools. They would also have a very good understanding of common devices available to solve electrical and mechanical problems. However, they would still lack some of the integrative skills required to make mechatronic design decisions, even after this extended education. Gaining an understanding of these fundamental skills should not wait until the fifth or sixth year of college education. It shouldn't even wait until junior year when most students move from a general engineering program to a specific program focused on chemical, mechanical, or electrical engineering. Core mechatronics skills can and should be taught from the very beginning of an education program. These skills can be included in standard electrical or mechanical engineering undergraduate courses without major impact to the amount of material covered.

In most course catalogs 90 percent of the material is devoted to descriptions of individual courses, with a few paragraphs that discuss the particular major itself. Rarely will the catalog address the unifying themes that run through each course. Even when educators discuss a topic that requires a multidepartmental approach they use language focused on individual courses instead of major themes that should transcend each course. However, a mechatronic engineer needs technology-independent skills that transcend each individual course. These skills are:

- System design
- Decision-making skills to weigh design alternatives
- Environment that supports risk taking
- How to work on a team

How can one teach decision-making skills, get students to work as a team, and develop projects that incorporate cross-functional collaboration? The task seems insurmountable. What follows is a discussion of how each of these skills, so critical to mechatronics engineering, can be taught from the very beginning of a college education.

5.2.1 System-level design

The heart of system-level design is the fundamental big-picture problem being solved, whether it is transmission assembly, money counting, or an antilock brake system. Forgetting the fundamental problem can lead to a specific functional solution that does not provide the best overall system solution. By looking at the large picture, many times a solution can be found for the problem which develops a far simpler total solution than if each aspect of the problem is solved in isolation.

The invention of the remote compliant center (RCC) by Paul Watson and Sam Drake is an example, though inadvertent, of system-level problem solving. Watson and Drake were actually trying to develop a force-sensing robot end effector that could facilitate the assembly of transmissions. The force-sensing end effector was not completed, so the pair decided to create a simple end effector to study the assembly problem. After programming a robot to assemble the transmission, they realized that force sensing in the end effector was not needed. The robot could simply assemble the transmission every time. Further analysis of the robot and the assembly operation revealed that there was sufficient backlash in the robot drives and flexibility in the robot linkages to allow for compliance in the assembly operation itself. The realization that compliance was a key to assembly led Watson and Drake to design the RCC. The RCC allowed robots that were very rigid to have the necessary compliance at the end effector so that even very rigid robots could perform the transmission assembly operation.

Some universities do this by offering a system-level design course in the freshman year. This course is typically very challenging because the students lack the fundamental skills necessary to come up with some of the design alternatives. Nevertheless students can operate at a conceptual level, possibly using lego sets with motors and discrete switches, instead of machined parts and programmable logic controllers.

Above and beyond a freshman year system design course, keeping track of the bigger picture is something that can be reinforced in each class. Classes can be structured so that discrete problems are viewed as parts of a larger problem. For example, instead of teaching calculus as a separate topic, Carnegie Mellon University now teaches differential calculus as part of the sophomore electrical engineering course. Concurrent focus on the higher-level design problems while learning discrete skills reinforces the notion of system design throughout the curriculum.

Another strategy is to teach students to look for solutions to problems across multiple engineering domains. For example, a money-counting machine could use mechanical means to trap and straighten money. The mechanical solution to deskewing might involve mechanical stops and a sensor for each note. This solution would be slow and have the tendency to damage some of the notes. Looking for an electronic device to sense skewed notes could lead to any number of mechatronic solutions including one that might allow the counting machine to be made at less cost, with better integrity of the notes and with a far higher throughput.

In the freshman year the solutions and range of alternatives that students have at their fingertips may be very limited. The range of solutions can be filled out as the academic training proceeds. The important thing is to instill the correct mind-set to search for as wide a range as possible of solutions from the start of the design effort. Engineering students can also be taught, through case studies, to expand their search for solutions.

System-level design can also be taught by example. Lab exercises and lectures can include examples from multiple disciplines. For example, an exercise in the analysis of various linkages can include an electrical solenoid. Certain pivots in the linkages can have rotary optical grates attached to them. The student would be required to determine the relative angle of the linkages in terms of a certain number of grid lines in the optical grate. Or a basic class on digital logic can use optical detectors to count the number of interrupts received. This exercise would readily tie into a basic class in digital logic design. Finally, a class in simulation can simulate both the electronic and mechanical aspects of a product design instead of only the mechanical aspects, as is typically done.

5.2.2 Decision-making skills to weigh design alternatives

Given the wide array of product design alternatives available with a mechatronic approach, it becomes critical to give students the skills necessary to weigh design alternatives and decide which option is the most satisfactory for the particular product. Without these skills a student will become overwhelmed by potential choices and will prefer to quickly lock onto one idea to the exclusion of all others. Typically students fresh out of school can readily develop new ideas, but what they need is the ability to evaluate which ideas should be pursued to the next level of detail.

Today these decisions quite often require choices between radically different design alternatives. In the past products could be safely designed without requiring extensive engineering judgment. To compensate for that lack of analysis, products were typically designed with excessive product content (e.g., materials, engine horsepower, gear size). The world was also much safer because products typically involved fewer design disciplines.

For example, turn-of-the-century music boxes had a mechanism similar to a clock—a spring to provide a force, and a set a reduction gears that ultimately turned a plate or drum that in turn caused various notes to be played. Many of the "clock" mechanisms of these early music boxes had massive parallel plates that sandwiched an only slightly less massive system of gears. This construction was typical of designs where it was cheaper to construct the product with too much material than do the engineering required to determine the appropriate strengths for the mounting plate and gears.

The world has changed drastically. Reduced material and manufacturing costs, lightness in weight, and increased functions have all led to a very heavy demand on the up-front engineering time required for product design. Couple that with competitive pressures to design products in an ever-shorter design cycle and we clearly have a situation where poor decisions can be made. Many of these mistakes can and must be minimized by teamwork, understanding of process, and design tools. However, good analysis and decision-making skills are the keys to making the right decisions the first time. Many quick techniques such as cost matrices or Pareto diagrams can be used to help make decisions. Homework and lab exercises can be set up to force students to use these tools any time there is a decision to be made. This in turn requires assignments to be structured to actually have alternate solutions to a problem. These decision matrices or Pareto diagrams can be linked back to system-level design or customer requirements by using a more sophisticated decision-making model such as the decision matrices found in the quality functional deployment approach.

5.2.3 Environment that supports risk taking

Today, industry needs engineers who are willing to try alternate technology to design less costly products with equivalent or greater functionality. And they must risk making these decisions while under pressure for innovation and decreased time to market. Finally, they must take these risks without benefit of all the relevant information. (As Lee Iacocca said[2] in 1984, "An engineer must make decisions with only 80% of the information in hand. Collecting the final 20% can take so long that the market has completely changed.")

Under these conditions, the only way to move a company forward is to establish an environment where it is all right to take risks as long as one learns from the mistakes. This means that failures must be an accepted part of the culture, especially since most companies will have only one success out of ten attempts.[3]

So what can a university do to give engineers a better understanding of the need for risk taking? Just as the commercial world revolves around the dollar, the academic world (from the perspective of the students) revolves around grades. Clearly the professor can't start giving A's or 4.0's to the students who take the greatest number of risks. Even in risk-promoting companies the person who develops the successful product will receive more awards than the person who has taken more risks but failed. So is it acceptable for a university to place risk-taking students who are failing or aren't getting the best mark into some isolated tutorial where they are the only persons who can benefit from the mistakes? Definitely not! Typically, something that is not well understood by one student is not well understood by others. Students need to discuss their misunderstandings in an open environment. Likewise if a student has failed a project or a test then his or her failures need to be brought up as a learning example for all the other students in the class. Universities can allow students to take risks and maintain their grade system by establishing student teams. If the students receive a grade based on the efforts of the team, then individual members will feel freer to explore more ideas. The team can present the best idea from the team. In the meantime they may have explored several ideas and used some of the decision-making tools to help choose from the possible solutions. Some of the possible solutions prove to be the riskier solutions that would not have been possible to propose in an environment where each student was competing for his or her own grade.

Working in teams also allows students to come up with off-the-wall ideas without feeling pressured or embarrassed by the presence of a professor. This same notion is often used in industry for peer reviews. In such an industrial peer review managers are typically not invited. Without managers around participants are not as inclined to become defensive when risky ideas or mistakes are discussed by the team. Harvard Business School[4] has only recently started to change its reward system to shift from a warfarelike competition among individual students to team collaboration.

5.2.4 Teamwork

Industry desperately wants engineers that can work effectively on teams. In a recent survey of 1000 employers conducted by the National Society of Professional Engineers an overwhelming 8 out of 10 employers placed a high value on teamwork.[5] No wonder when one considers that industry is trying to embrace concepts such as mechatronics, concurrent engineering, or design for manufacturing which all share a very important common theme—teamwork. However, getting students to work together as a team is difficult, especially in the structure of many universities. Universities have two very significant teamwork road blocks. First, the departmental focus keeps an aspiring mechatronics student focused within a particular discipline or department. Second, the reward system focuses on grades for the individual student instead of the team.

Let's turn briefly to an environment where teamwork is absolutely essential. Consider the sport of swimming. In individual races such as the 1650-meter freestyle the audience focuses on the lead swimmer. In some cases the last swimmer finishes several minutes behind the winner. By this time all attention has turned away from the pool to the winner strolling around on the pool deck. In a relay event such as the individual medley four swimmers must work together. Rewards are given only to the team with the best overall winning time, not to the fastest swimmer in a particular stroke. If the medley relay team wants to improve, they will focus on the slowest part of the race and try to improve this particular aspect so as to improve the team's overall performance.

Industry works the same way as the medley relay team. Stand-alone brilliance will not create a winning product that sells well in the marketplace. The winning company is the one that has the best overall winning team, with electrical engineering, mechanical engineering, marketing, and sales all working together.

Universities must train their students to work in a team environment. The team concept was discussed earlier in this book; however, several techniques can help build an understanding of how to work as a team within the university environment. The first and most obvious approach is to actually promote the concept of teams. One simple example is to allow students to work together on their homework. Earl M. Murman has taken this approach, challenging MIT's "do it or die"[1] policy by allowing students to work together on homework.

A related approach is to promote the concept of a team through the reward system. The biggest reward system at a university is based on grades. Grades could be based on both the individual's grade and the grade for the team. Students would be motivated to make sure that the team is functioning well in addition to ensure their own performance. Finally training in team skills can be initiated in the freshman year to teach students how teams work, how different personality types affect overall team dynamics, or how to manage conflict. These skills could then be reinforced in different class situations as teams are formed and disbanded. In the real world students will move in and out of many teams throughout their careers. Therefore, schools should make sure that a student is not always part of the same group throughout the whole degree program. This is in sharp contrast to the previous practices of Harvard Business School, where students were broken into two large classes and then further broken down into study teams that might remain intact throughout the degree program.

So far in this section nothing has been mentioned about specific topics of study. This is because true mechatronics needs the philosophies of a multidiscipline, team-oriented approach to problem solving. These disciplines must be taught as a common theme in every class the student takes so that they are reinforced across the entire engineering curriculum. Recommendations for specific courses to be taught at the undergraduate level are discussed in greater detail later.

5.3 Mechatronics at the Graduate Level

Once basic skills such as teamwork, and weighing design alternatives and basic technologies such as basic machine design, digital electronics, and control theory have been learned, the student is ready to refine these skills at the graduate level. Specific projects could take the graduate student through an actual design cycle. Typically the design of a full product will be too much to tackle, but certainly a redesign or the addition of a feature might be reasonable. Graduates students can also assume leadership positions in lab exercises for undergraduates. For example, if a particular mechanical engineering course has a lab, a graduate student can help the teams develop their decision-making and team-participation skills. Graduate students can also help undergraduates stretch their imaginations to include design choices other than those presented in the actual text.

The graduate level also provides the student with the opportunity to refine the skills and technology developed in the undergraduate program. Basic decision matrix skills can be refined with a class in Quality Functional Deployment (QFD). The QFD analysis performed by the graduate student could form a basis for the lab exercises performed by undergraduate students.

5.4 Industrial Training in Mechatronics

Until universities can turn out engineers sufficiently cross-trained in multiple disciplines and in an integrated approach to system design, industry must pick up the training slack. Clearly from a discrete skills point of view a company should encourage its employees to go back to school for classes in the disciplines in which they have no formal training. (A description of the types of courses that could help follows later in this chapter.) This is especially common for electrical or mechanical engineers who graduated over 10 years ago, prior to the wide-scale introduction of embedded microprocessors. They realize that to remain competitive they must broaden their backgrounds to include training in other disciplines. In some cases a local university might offer the necessary courses. In other cases the student may participate in a course by viewing videotapes of the actual lectures or listening in to the lecture by phone. Many universities offer such programs. To build the more general skills required for mechatronics, the company must provide its own training and supporting environments.

System-level design knowledge can be built in each employee by keeping each team member aware of the bigger picture. Even if the individual employee is not making decisions that directly affect system-level design, hearing about the decisions and how they were reached enables individuals to make better design suggestions that consider the goals of the system, as well as better decisions for their own piece of the design. This awareness of system-level details also helps to train employees for the day they will be required to take on system-level design themselves.

Team building can be taught and supported by actually creating teams in the workplace. It is a good idea to couple this formation of teams with formal training in how to work in teams. Some of the topics to be trained on are covered later in this section. In a large company multidisciplinary teams can be built in which, for example, the electronic engineer works directly with the mechanical engineer to solve heat-loss problems upsetting the stable temperature required for electronic components of the product. In a small company, designing ventilation, mounting brackets, and printed circuit board layout could be assigned to one person, who effectively becomes a one-person team.

Most importantly, as has already been emphasized in the preceding section, the company needs to foster an environment in which mechatronics can succeed. What good would it do electrical engineers to take a course in basic mechanical mechanisms if their job assignments are restricted to their electrical functional silo? A junior electrical engineer bemoaned the shortsightedness of the manager who would say, "I don't know what you're taking that course for, you'll never use those skills in this department." The course in question was in structured programming. The engineer felt that it would give a better appreciation for the difficulties faced by the microprocessor coders. Clearly mechatronics won't succeed unless the company endorses the concept and establishes an environment in which it can succeed.

5.5 Curriculum Guidelines

This chapter would not be complete without specific course curriculum recommendations.

5.5.1 Overall curriculum structure

There are two ways to structure the overall mechatronic engineering curriculum: top-down or bottom-up. In the top-down structure students start with a system design course, even though they do not yet possess the skills to do detailed analysis or come up with alternate design strategies. The bottom-up approach gives students all the necessary training in control theory, mechanical devices, and embedded microprocessors, then builds on these lower-level blocks until the student can design an overall system. In practice industry uses a combination of both strategies. System designers *are* system designers because they have many years of experience. They can quickly judge the impact of their up-front design decisions because they know from experience the various implementation details. Entry-level engineers are apt to focus on specific bottom-up implementation details. Even though both approaches are required, industry needs people that have a better appreciation for the top-down level of design so that the designers are more aware of the impact their decisions have on the whole product design. In the university setting there isn't enough time to collect a wealth of design experience, nor is there time for students to participate in multiple product design cycles. Yet at the heart of every product is the notion that each decision is made in the context of the larger system design. Because this design mentality must be instilled from the beginning, a true mechatronics undergraduate curriculum should be structured in a top-down fashion. This means the cross-functional skills of system design, decision analysis, and team interaction should be taught at the freshman level. From this freshman base these basic skills are reinforced and complemented with specific functional skills.

5.5.2 Undergraduate curriculum

A great deal of thought has been put into mechatronics undergraduate curriculum design by educators around the world. The following course recommendations are a synthesis of curricula developed at Louisiana State University, City Polytechnic of Hong Kong, and Dundee Institute of Technology, among others. A union of all these curricula would satisfy everyone except the students, who would like to be able to graduate in 4 years. The following courses are recommended to be taught in a mechatronics undergraduate curriculum. It is important to note that students could actually spend several semesters on a topic such as Machine Design, Control, or Computers and Embedded Microprocessors.

Programming
Control
Man-Machine Interfaces
Robots and Automation
Design for Manufacture
Computers and Embedded Microprocessor
Machine Communications and Interfaces
Machine Design
Computer-Aided Engineering
Hands-on Work

5.5.2.1 Programming I. As with many of these courses, Programming, or Software Engineering, can lead to a profession unto itself. As any professional software engineer would say, there is a right way and a wrong way to develop software. This course must emphasize the "right" way. Recommendations on the approach can be found in guidelines formed by the Software Engineering Institutes framework, which describes an ideal software development approach. In reality the approach is a design methodology developed to shift software development away from "hacking" and toward an engineering "profession." This design process, which emphasizes system-level design, could actually be applied to the entire mechatronic design process.

Within the context of a methodical design process where software follows design there are the details of programming itself. Students typically receive their first introduction to programming through a course in C, C++, Pascal, or Ada, for example. This course should also introduce the design that led to the particular software programming lectures. This should be the first course taught so that students learn structured programming before entering the less structured world of microprocessor programming.

The next course (described below) should be in microprocessor software development, bringing the student much closer to the hardware, in terms of both the development cycle and the end product.

5.5.2.2 Computers and embedded microprocessors. This particular course should be a high-level overview of microprocessor architecture and operation. It would cover topics such as interrupt systems, register addressing, instruction sets, interfacing to memory, bus design and interprocess and task communication schemes, all the time referring back to the specific microprocessor chosen for the target project. It could also cover issues such as hardware solutions for data transmission and signal processing. Practically it helps to discuss specific examples of devices so that students have some practical experience with the selection of various microprocessors, digital to analog and analog to digital (DA and AD) converters, opto-isolators, etc., used in the processing and transmission of signals. This course should teach the student how to develop microprocessor programs on a host PC or other system, download these programs to an emulator, and finally burn them into a ROM device so it can be run on the target machine. The relationship is depicted in Fig. 5.1.

5.5.2.3 Control. This course should focus on three main areas, data acquisition, data handling, and control theory. Data acquisition gives the students an understanding of the wide variety of sensors and transducers available to measure various conditions. Data handling

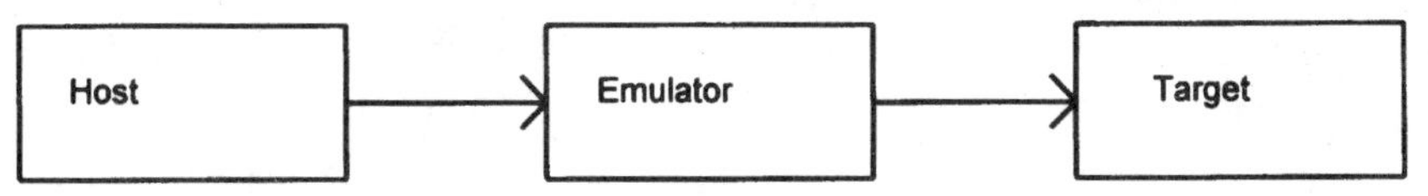

Figure 5.1 Course relationship.

discusses the signal processing problems involved in processing the collected data. Finally control theory focuses on how to control the device itself. A thorough discussion of open and closed loop control strategies, transfer functions, and digital control algorithms should be included in this final area.

5.5.2.4 Machine communication and interfaces. The Computers and Embedded Microprocessors course briefly touches on electronic means of processing signals received from various sensors. This course is designed to cover the full signal transmission and machine interfacing issue in greater detail. It considers pretransmission signal processing strategies and representations, signal transmission strategies, and final signal collection strategies. Initial signal processing should discuss various devices that include embedded signal processors such as the accelerometer depicted in Fig. 5.2. Signal representations analog and digital and their representations should be defined. These signal representations can then be discussed relative to various mediums used for signal transmission—wires, fiber optic, and radio communications as examples. Mechatronic systems that must communicate with other products using protocols such as MAP, Ethernet, and RS232 should also be discussed. Finally signal capturing can focus on receipt of these signals and further signal process.

Most of the pre- and posttransmission signal process involves quantitization and noise reduction. Quantitization discussions can focus on what type of signal—digital, analog, or gray code discrete pulses—is needed to capture system information. Noise reduction must be discussed because it enters into each phase of the machine communication process and affects the choices for signal representation and signal transmission.

The course should also cover how machines can be designed to determine whether they are behaving according to plan. Techniques used to measure accelerations, speeds, etc., are all valuable in determining whether the machine is operating per design.

5.5.2.5 Man-machine interface design. Man-Machine Interface Design should present a detailed list of possible mechanisms for machine-to-man interaction—video terminals, heads-up displays, analog gauges, selector switches, touch screen displays, joy sticks, and mice, to name a few. The course should also consider the ergonomic decisions that affect the choice of devices. Issues such as hostility of the environment, speed of interaction, and ability of the operator to remain focused should be considered. This course should present the possibilities for man-machine interaction in the context of industrial examples that illustrate their use. The course should also give stu-

Figure 5.2 Accelerometer.

dents the necessary tools to evaluate choices best suited for various environments and types of operator interaction.

Many industrial examples, from numerical control machines with both industrially rugged push button interaction and video display of cutter paths, to jet aircraft cockpit design, can illustrate different combinations of environment and man-machine device selections. These industrial examples should also illustrate how "style" affects the overall man-machine interaction.

5.5.2.6 Machine design. Mechatronics requires that the engineer make trade-offs between the electronic, control, and mechanical designs in the product. Without a good background in machine design the student will not be able to make these decisions. Machine design should give students an understanding of common mechanical devices or components from which machines are built. The course focuses on the transmission and generation of motion, as well as the surrounding structural rigidity of the product.

5.5.2.7 Robots and automation. Robots and Automation should be presented as two industrial areas that rely heavily on mechatronics. The discussion of robotics should define various types of robots and how control theory and machine design were integrated to solve industrial problems.

Robots, as U.S. engineers think of them, are only part of the mechatronic examples found in manufacturing. Other automation, which accounts for a large part of the Japanese installed robot base, also offers many examples of mechatronics. Automation topics should include individual CNC machines, FMSs, AGVs, and other part transport systems.

5.5.2.8 Computer-aided engineering. Most companies today are trying to develop their new products using computer-aided engineering (CAE) techniques. (A fair amount of Chapter 6 is devoted to various forms of SW Tools available to the mechatronics engineer.) This course should include a survey of the technologies available for design (modeling techniques), analysis tools (digital and analog simulations, finite element analysis), and manufacturing. Some time should be spent on rapid prototyping with stereolithography or other techniques. Hands-on time should be spent on a project where students actually use a CAE product to create their designs. This course should be introduced as early as possible so that the CAE tools can be used in later courses and labs.

5.5.2.9 Design for life cycle costs. A few years back this class would have been called "Design for Manufacturing." Today's engineers must build products that consider the full life cycle of the product. A company incurs costs when the product is designed, manufactured, serviced, and finally retired. The focus on costs incurred late in the product life cycle is being driven by competitive pressures and customer service orientation as well as legislation. For example, there is a movement in Europe to force companies to buy back their products at the end of the products' life cycles, forcing the product designer to facilitate recycling in its design. This course should introduce the design issues around "life cycle cost analysis" as well as tools that are available to help perform this analysis. Lab exercises can focus on design for assembly problems, as well as software tools such at those provided by Boothroyd Dewhurst Inc. to analyze suitability of designs for manufacturing and serviceability.

5.5.2.10 Hands-on work. One of the biggest criticisms of university programs, including those found in Japan, is that the students do not emerge with enough hands-on experience. The United Kingdom and United States have started to address this problem by developing "sandwich" or "co-op" programs in which students go out into industry and actually practice some of the skills they have learned.

Further, core curriculum must include lab work that gives students the opportunity to blow up an op-amp with too much current or inadvertently create an open-loop control situation due to feedback miswiring. These lab experiences give students an understanding of the types of instrumentation, voltage meters, oscilloscopes, NC mills and lathes, etc., that are commonly used in the design and test of products. The students also gain an appreciation of mechatronics through their lab work because many of the instruments used are themselves examples of mechatronic products.

Several examples of this hands-on approach can already be found in academia. The University of Minnesota has a Capstone Design project. This project allows the senior-level student to integrate all the knowledge gained throughout the past 3 years in a "cradle-to-grave design process, from defining customer needs to considering detailed technical and manufacturing needs."[6]

At the graduate level MIT has established the New Products Program. This program brings together graduate-level mechanical engineering students with students from the Sloan School of Management and industrial sponsors. These groups tackle real-life problems posed by the industrial sponsors in 2-year projects. Unlike make-work projects in other programs, this program actually focuses on projects that the sponsor companies view as critical to their futures. The sponsors view these projects as so critical that they assign company people full-time to the project. Students participate in a real-world design process which has all the problems of, for example, communication, schedules, or scope definition that projects carried out in industry would have. In conclusion, it is possible to create a mechatronic curriculum that teaches fundamental, single-focus skills *and* cross-functional skills necessary for mechatronic design. Likewise, industry can improve employees' abilities to develop mechatronic-based products by sponsoring education in specific topics, as well as creating a work environment in which mechatronics can succeed.

5.5.2.11 Accreditation. Accreditation of a university's engineering program creates a major roadblock in the development of a mechatronic curriculum. The Accreditation Board for Engineering and Technology (ABET) sets general guidelines for engineering. On top of that, each professional engineering society creates a set of course requirements specific to the society's discipline. By the time the ABET and the professional society have identified their requirements there is usually no opportunity for changes. Without a mechatronics professional society there is no way to specifically set guidelines for undergraduate curricula. The editorial in *Science*[7] suggests that one way to get out of this logjam is for ABET to reduce by 20 percent the number of courses it requires. This extra 20 percent of freedom could enable a university (or a student for that matter) to create a curriculum that crosses electromechanical boundaries.

References

1. "Coming off the Drawing Board: Better Engineers?" *Business Week*, Aug. 2, 1993, pp. 70–71.
2. Iacocca, Lee and William Novak: *Iacocca,* Bantam Books, New York, 1984, p. 54.
3. Peters, Thomas J. and Robert H. Waterman: *In Search of Excellence,* Warner Books, New York, 1982, p. 227.
4. "A Case Study in Change at Harvard," *Business Week,* Nov. 19, 1993, p. 42.
5. Dahir, Mubarak: "Educating Engineers for the Real World," *Technology Review,* August/September 1993, pp. 14–16.
6. Durfee, William: "Engineering Education Gets Real," *Technological Review,* February/March 1994, pp. 42–51.
7. Morgan, M. Granger: "Accreditation and Diversity in Engineering Education," *Science,* Aug. 31, 1990, p. 969.

Chapter

6

Software-Based Tools

Although a mechatronic approach can be achieved with very little, if any, automation or software tools, executing a mechatronic process is accelerated by the presence of software tools for use by mechanical, electrical, and software engineers. Appendix B lists the major software suppliers and describes their products.

This chapter is devoted to software tools that can assist in the execution of the mechatronic process. Products such as word processors, spreadsheets, and project management packages are viewed as too general to be considered in this chapter. The software tools available to the team are depicted in Fig. 6.1. This illustration is somewhat simplified to show the types of tools at a broad level. Additionally the tools and the timing of their use are referenced by the layout of the illustration from left to right. Customer requirements generate activity in two primary areas: schematic capture and computer three-dimensional model preparation. The initiation of these activities occurs at the same time. These tools need to be used as early in the development cycle as possible, starting with the concept stage. The tools and their capabilities are explored to give the reader an understanding of how they facilitate a mechatronic process.

6.1 Prepare Schematics and Analyze

The preparation of schematics has been occurring for some time. The primary purpose has been to support printed circuit board (PCB) design. Therefore, the schematics have had very much an "electronic" flavor. The schematic must broaden its capacities to address electrical-type functionality as well as strict electronic functionality. Functional requirements of the product, the features, and the capabilities that are needed are detailed using a schematic. This needs to be per-

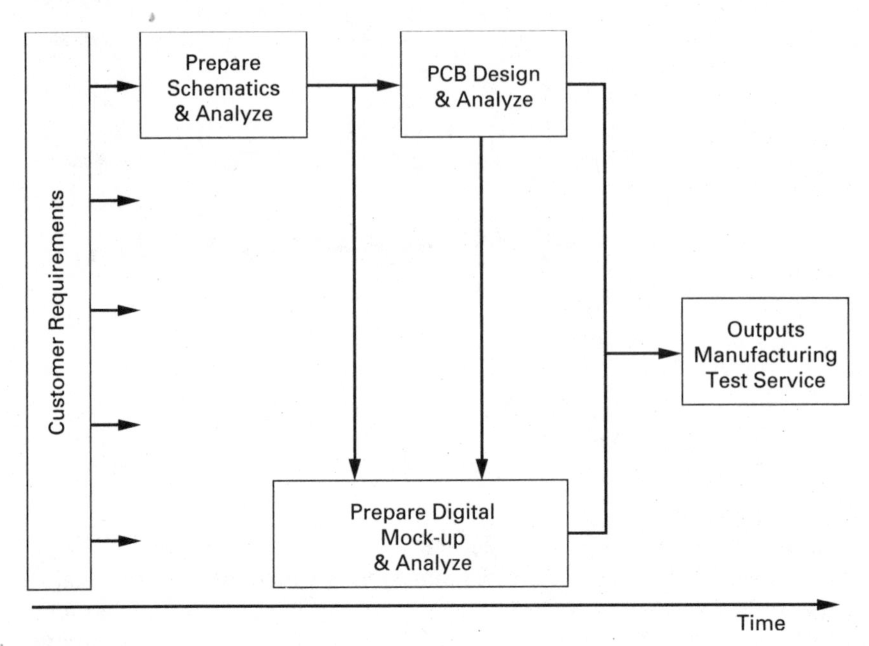

Figure 6.1 Software tools.

formed with a hierarchy so that systems and subsystems can be identified and specified. These systems and subsystems include an automobile's ignition system, braking system, and audio system or a plane's radar system, fuel system, and landing system.

One of the main purposes of the schematic is to show point-to-point connectivity for electronic components on a printed circuit board or connectivity for the entire board with a power supply board, or connectivity between an on-off switch and the power supply board.

Once the initial schematic is prepared, it can be analyzed. The analysis is of primarily two types:[1]

- Integrity checks
- Functionality simulation

The purpose of integrity checks is to find networks with unconnected ends, networks with inconsistent colors, network loops, unused terminals, undefined currents, duplicate components and network names, and undefined names of components and networks. The basic premise is to determine if the network is constructed to be complete. This analysis is performed on a hierarchical basis to check interconnection between components and board assemblies, as well as check proper connections between electronic components as part of the printed circuit board.

Software that simulates functionality enables the engineer to determine if the design performs the necessary functions, and to ensure it responds properly with a given set of inputs to yield the desired outputs. Optimally, the results are shown graphically to assist the engineering team. Additionally, this analysis can aid in the preparation of FTA (fault tree analysis) and FMEA (failure modes effects analysis). Further, to analyze the logic proposed for printed circuit boards, analog, digital, and mixed mode simulations can be conducted. Again, the purpose is to ensure the design functions as intended. This analysis helps prevent the need to prepare expensive prototypes which are prepared for the sole purpose of ensuring the design functions as intended.

Hence, the real advantage of schematic preparation and analysis is the ability to modify the design and determine the results—to perform "what if" analysis. Design trade-offs can be more easily evaluated. The result is that more trade-offs can be analyzed and therefore the probability that the logical design will be optimized is increased. This design optimization is only from a functional or logic perspective. This process needs to also consider other life cycle constraints to optimize the entire product design. These include physical package size and configuration, manufacturability, and serviceability constraints.

6.2 PCB Design and Analyze

The design of the printed circuit boards is based on the inputs from the schematic diagram. It consists primarily of performing layout of the electronic components and routing of signals. The basic objective is to fit many components in the smallest area possible. This is one of the areas where automation has played a major role for over 20 years. It provides significant increases in both efficiency and effectivity compared to manual methods.

However, many problems may result when density of electronic components becomes very high. These problems include electromagnetic interference and heating of the components, which alter the performance of the components and system. Therefore, the printed circuit board needs to be analyzed under multiple conditions to reduce the electromagnetic interference and heating problems.

Software is readily available from multiple suppliers to perform the analysis. Additionally, a manufacturer may use a third party company to perform the analysis, if in-house capability does not exist. It is critical to perform this analysis to optimize the design, so that other more expensive measures are not needed. More expensive measures to deal with heating problems include adding cooling fans to dissipate the heat and adding vents to allow the heat to be released. Methods to reduce or eliminate electromagnetic interference include shielding components or adding shield barriers after the fact. These measures are expensive and possibly could be avoided with comprehensive analysis performed early in the development cycle.

6.3 Prepare Digital Mock-up and Analyze

Engineers at many manufacturing firms are using a tool called a digital mock-up (also referred to as digital preassembly, electronic mock-up, and electronic preassembly).[2–4] Digital mock-ups are three-dimensional computer representations of complete products or systems. They allow engineers to evaluate mechanical and electrical constraints simultaneously in an intuitive visual format. Digital mock-ups contain models of all components and assemblies that comprise a product, including mechanical (structures and enclosures) and electronic-electrical (printed circuit boards, switches, sensors, relays, wires). They facilitate the design of the package to house the internal components. Many designs present packaging challenges and require a method to solve the problem. "Squeezing the powertrain, suspension, control systems and other components under the short, low-cowl was the JA-platform (Chrysler Cirrus) team's biggest challenge."[5] A good package was achieved as a result of teamwork and computer (three-dimensional digital mock-ups).

Digital mock-ups are the drawing boards of the future that are available today, the medium for communication among engineers. As designs evolve, mock-ups clearly show changes, and these changes can be quickly evaluated. The use of digital mock-ups increases productivity and minimizes mistakes.

Using digital mock-ups, for example, electrical engineers can design electronic assemblies and immediately determine if they fit within the product. Mechanical engineers, on the other hand, can evaluate physical clearances with respect to electromagnetic interference or any other electrical constraint.

With the preparation of digital mock-ups and their components, assemblies, and systems, the "master" is now prepared. The model is the master and is linked to all other operations such as drafting and detailing, stress analysis, mechanisms analysis, and numerical control as shown in Fig. 6.2. These operations directly use the geometry created using the digital mock-up which is created with all project personnel inputs to prepare drawings and perform up-front stress

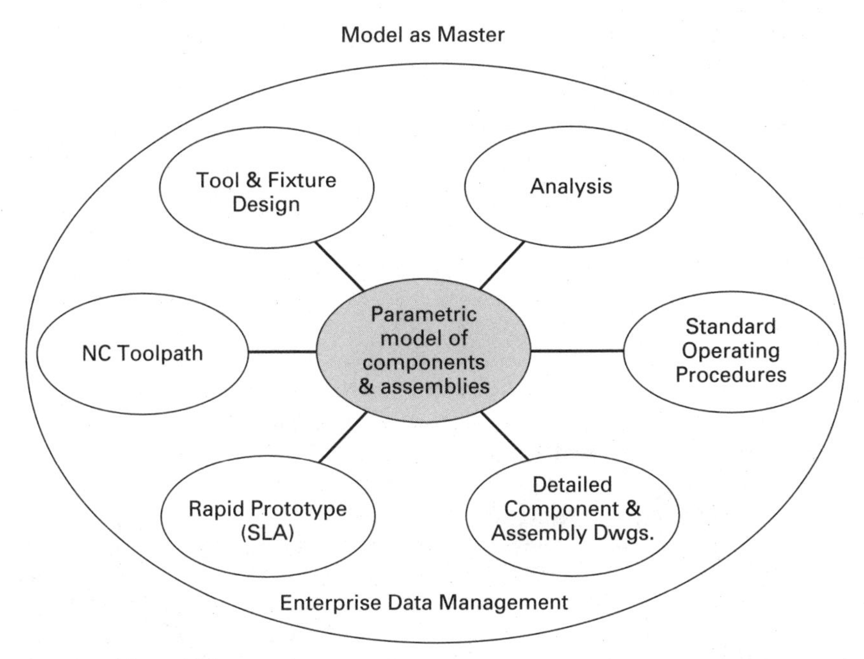

Figure 6.2 The model as master.

analysis, mechanisms analysis, and prepare and verify job control files for numerical control equipment.

The links between the model and these applications are parametric and associative so that a change in the model cascades throughout the other operations.

More specific to drafting, the use of three-dimensional modeling techniques provides free multiple drawing views (right side, top front, etc.). When a drawing consists of several views and the model is changed, the views are automatically updated. The user does not have to update the views based on the changes made to the models. Furthermore, a change to one view is reflected in all other views.

The model geometry created using a digital mock-up can be used for generating finite element meshes and then performing analysis on the specific geometry. This analysis includes stress and thermal analysis. When the model is modified, the changes are reflected in the finite element geometry and the previously created mesh.

Specifically applicable to numerical control, the same geometry created using solid modeling techniques and digital mock-up methodologies can be used to design the machining operations to manufacture the applicable components. This manufacturing sequence could be defined by supplier (both external and internal) based on a file containing the model geometry. When a model is modified, the machining sequence can be automatically updated to reflect the change.

Without a 3D model, using the digital mock-up techniques above, the operations previously described must happen in sequence as opposed to being performed in parallel. The digital mock-up is the medium facilitating this simultaneous activity.

Once a strong foundation has been established including structural and enclosure components, the digital mock-up preparation can be completed by adding 3D models of electronic components and assemblies, interconnection components such as wires, cables, and harnesses. The objective, as stated by Short Brothers, is to sandwich components into the wing, ensuring there are no clashes.[6] This can be accomplished only with a digital mock-up. Using the digital mock-up was a great leap forward.

At this stage of the digital mock-up all major components and assemblies are modeled, and more importantly, electrical engineering and mechanical engineering personnel have a medium to communicate effectively and consider each discipline's constraints. This is done in development as opposed to pilot production via the use of traditional physical mock-ups. A proactive approach can be implemented using a digital mock-up, as opposed to a reactive approach associated with a physical mock-up, when a design is modified after a problem results. Problems can be prevented since electrical engineering and mechanical engineering personnel can work in harmony using a consistent medium, the digital mock-up.

The digital mock-up becomes the medium for all personnel working on a project to use as a reference when designing their particular components or subassemblies. It enables design engineers and other project personnel such as manufacturing engineers to work concurrently on the same design and to determine the effect of a specific engineer's output on the rest of the project team. The consequences of someone's actions can be quickly viewed and evaluated for correctness.

One of the key advantages of preparing a digital mock-up is the ability to perform interference checks. "Boeing engineers pre-assembled the 777 aircraft to check for part interferences."[7] Specific problem parts are identified by part number so that the modification process is accelerated. Additionally, since assembly requires equipment and fixturing, the digital mock-up can be utilized to determine equipment clearances required during assembly processes. Boeing uses a human factors model which enables engineers to check the accessibility of parts and systems requiring maintenance on the 777.[4] Exploded view drawings can be created to assist manufacturing personnel. Constraints for maintainability and repairability can also be evaluated using the digital mock-up. Volvo GM Heavy Truck Corp. claims that maintenance times have decreased because of the access to mechanical and electrical engineering data facilitated by a digital mock-up.[8]

Additionally, assembly design or electronic preassembly technology can be utilized to lay out a project early in development in terms of its high-level subassemblies and systems. At this stage space can be allocated for particular systems, subassemblies, and components. As the design evolves and more detail becomes available the assembly structure can be refined from space allocation to reflect specific geometry regarding components and subassemblies that comprise the systems.

Once the digital mock-up is prepared, modifications are necessary, and trade-off analysis is needed to optimize the design. Modifying a physical mock-up is very time-consuming, perhaps taking days or even weeks to complete the modification of the physical mock-up. In contrast, modifying a digital mock-up is an order of magnitude less in terms of time to alter. Producing the first digital mock-up is probably not significantly less than producing a physical mock-up because of learning curve, etc. However, the time and cost to modify the digital mock-up are significantly less than the time associated with modifying the physical mock-up.

As more and more project development is automated, 3D geometric data and product structures are available for use on new projects. Leaders of the new projects are able to easily identify the necessary systems, components, and assemblies which can be copied from an archived database of projects. The new project consists of components, assemblies, and systems from previous contracts. Using assembly design product structure the lead engineer can easily identify the required components, assemblies, etc., for the new design.

Once the desired product structures are identified, the related geometry can be viewed in and oriented to create the base for the new design. Parts databases are minimized because the same component and subassembly can be used on several designs without duplicating the parts.

Last, with the availability of product databases that include part structures and cost, the process of bidding on a contract can be facilitated. The information contained in the product structure can be enhanced to include historical cost information so that the person preparing the bid can use the information to prepare a more accurate bid. This increases competitiveness, streamlines the process, and ensures acceptable profitability is achieved.

Analysis can and should be performed on the 3D structure, including assemblies and components, to optimize the design. Much of the effort to optimize the design through the use of finite element analysis has been automated. Design optimization routines automate the tasks of revising, remeshing, and reevaluating models to achieve the goals of the development team and meet customer requirements.[9] "The optimization routine governs the computer's evaluation of successive models, ultimately converging on an optimized design," based on user inputs.[9] Basically, optimization solutions eliminate the drudgery commonly associated with traditional iterative design and engineering. This analysis typically includes application of finite element meshing to determine heat transfer, or stress on a product. Analysis can vary from simulation of the mechatronic product itself to visualization of the man-machine interface, to detecting potential EMI/EMC problems.

6.4 Manufacturability and Serviceability Tools

As previously discussed, manufacturability and serviceability are key life cycle constraints which must be considered early in the development cycle, especially in the concept and technical feasibility stages. Guidelines were established to assist the development team. To improve the productivity of the development team when evaluating manufacturability and serviceability, software tools are available. Referred to as DFMA (design for manufacturability and assembly) and DFS (design for serviceability), these tools were developed in the early 1980s by Dr. Boothroyd and Dr. Dewherst.[10]

"Both DFS and DFMA focus on the concept stage of design engineering where changes are inexpensive and where 70% or more of a product's assembly and manufacturing costs are determined."[10] The concepts are strongly related and, in fact, DFS builds upon DFMA. Many companies including Ford, Caterpillar, Chrysler, Emerson Electric, Digital Equipment, and Hewlett-Packard are among the members of a group called Design for Dis-Assembly, Service and Environment Consortium.[10] It is not a coincidence that most of these companies manufacture products that contain electrical and mechanical components and assemblies.

DFMA software provides the capability to identify the most appropriate assembly system for a new product considering the structural analysis of the design relative to its overall efficiency and suitability for the selected method of assembly.[11] The software is a "methodology and data base system that allows the cross functional team to analyze and rate product design for ease of assembly and structural efficiency, as well as predict assembly and manufacturing costs."[11] Ultimately, the most feasible manufacturing process is identified. Codex, a division of Motorola, has used DFMA for several years to optimize the design of mechanical enclosures and printed circuit boards on its line of modems and networking systems.[11]

DFS software provides the development team with total disassembly and reassembly times, a serviceability rating index, and definition of critical serviceability costs including components and assembly, replacement, and labor costs.[10] The commonality with DFMA is the fact that a major determinant of serviceability is disassembly.

6.4.1 PCB design for manufacturability

One such design tool that directly serves the mechatronic engineer's needs has been created by Boothroyd Dewhurst Incorporated. The "PCB Design for Assembly Product" allows PCB designers to extend their focus from electrical integrity of the PCB to the manufacturing cost impacts of the PCB layout. This tool allows the PCB designer to consider such things as:

- Board size analysis to determine the manufacturability given a particular size board. One can also play what if scenarios by altering the board size to determine what effect that has on manufacturing costs.
- Quality labor analysis to spot parts that typically require extra rework.
- Analysis of percentage of board that can be manufactured with auto-insertable components.
- This analysis can help the electronic engineer start to wear the hats of both the mechanical engineer who is trying to design the PCBs to fit into a product, as well as the manufacturing engineer.

6.5 Outputs

A specific area which could be improved would be manufacturing by having rasterized drawings (standard operating procedures, assembly drawings, etc.) available on PCs right on the assembly floor to assist their efforts. This would replace the pieces of paper presently used as assembly instructions. It would enable control of these data so that correct instructions and illustration aids are utilized.

All the necessary model data can be extracted and rasterized, edited, and instructions identified to be used directly by manufacturing personnel. The master is the model or digital mock-up which includes all structural details, from/to information, wire lists, etc., to facilitate manufacturing activity. Furthermore, all these data can be managed by engineering data management software to ensure correctness during the manufacturing process.

The electronic data from 3D models and schematics can be used for manufacturing and assembly drawings. These documents are still the lifeblood for assembly and manufacturing, as well as being the reference for suppliers and customers. This is changing slowly, so that electronic data are exchanged between customer and supplier, via EDI (electronic data interchange). This information is readily available, and if changes are made to the model or schematic, they are reflected on the drawings by automatically updating the drawings.

The data related to the conditions which were used for simulation and analysis can be used as the input conditions for test equipment. The results of the tests can then be compared to the results achieved during the simulations and analyses. These results can then be used to refine the simulations and analyses. A closed-loop process results.

Using these data would obviously help manufacturing, but it also helps engineering personnel understand the problems encountered by manufacturing. It is a win win situation for all personnel involved!

6.6 Interoperability

Many traditional design tools on the market today assist an engineer to move the design from the concept through to manufacturing and support. These tools have been well established within the separate independent disciplines of mechanical and electrical engineering. Many suppliers of software exist to address the needs of electrical and mechanical engineers. As a result, there are basically two main interoperability issues:

- Interoperability among a specific discipline, such as mechanical engineering software packages. This will be referred to as intradiscipline interoperability.
- Interoperability among software of different disciplines, such as mechanical and electrical engineering. This will be referred to as interdiscipline interoperability.

In either case, the goal is to get software packages to share the data without conversions, etc. This is the highest level of integration possible; thus full interoperability is achieved.

6.6.1 Intradiscipline interoperability

On the mechanical engineering side are many tools to design NC cutter paths or analyze the flow of a plastic into a mold or analyze a process used to manufacture a part. On the electrical side is a set of software tools that can assist the electrical engineer in getting a product through manufacturing. For example, there are silicon compilers that will take a design and develop the actual masks used in the process of making chips. There are tools that will generate the NC drilling operations required to cut vias into a PCB or create insertion programs for automatic IC insertion equipment. There are now beginning to emerge a set of tools that bridge the gap between mechanical and electrical engineering.

Customers may solve problems through the use of a single supplier. But what happens when product developers require tools from different companies? A mechatronic process is possible even here, using a consistent environment such as a framework. Frameworks allow third party, proprietary, and custom tools to be integrated seamlessly into the design process. They also provide a user interface that gives all tools a common look and feel.

Not all frameworks are suited for mechatronics. Some are limited to electronic; others are limited to mechanical design. Development teams may work in a cooperative environment and share data. Equally important, the tools that they use must interoperate as well. "Thus, each mechanical CAD/CAM (MCAD) and electronic design automation (EDA) tool must incorporate the other tools' design in the models produced."[12] There are a few tools, however, which operate across multidisciplinary applications, facilitating mechanical and electronic design knowledge. The real question which begs to be asked is when does an integrated environment become a true mechatronic environment? For a mechatronic environment, a framework must support both EDA and MCAD tools. A framework that supports one or the other handicaps the engineer when modeling of both environments is required. Additionally, the tools themselves must operate consistently such as command procedures working in the same manner. For example, do control bars and pull-down menus have the same look? Are status messages formatted the same? Easy-to-use file management capabilities must be provided.[12]

The interoperability of the software can be facilitated in several ways. At the most fundamental level the data can be exchanged between applications. At the highest level a common user interface allows each application to appear the same to the product designer (see Fig. 6.3).

In the electronic design automation industry the regularity of the product being designed has allowed niche software vendors to create products that can readily communicate with one another at the data exchange layer. Some of the larger EDA vendors have then created

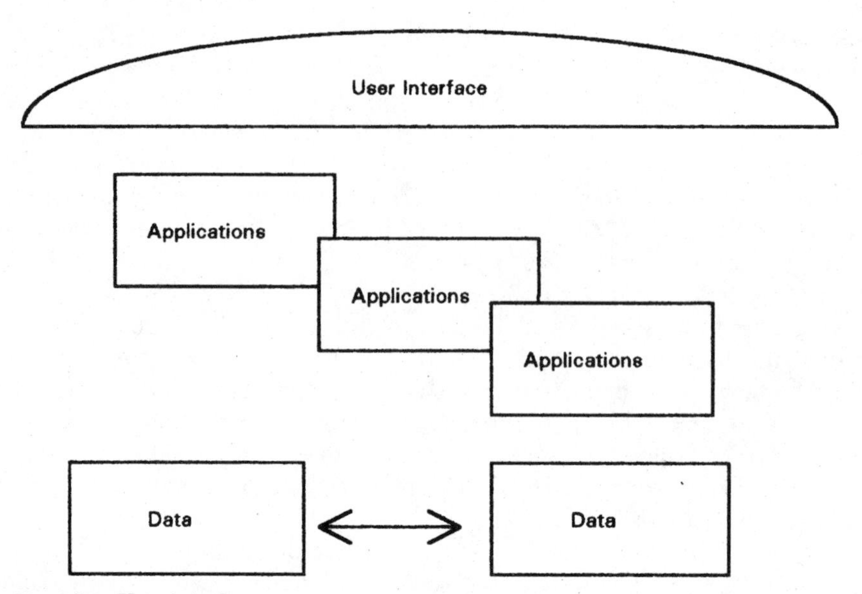

Figure 6.3 User interface.

user interfaces (frameworks), which allow multiple niche products to interoperate under one seamless user interface.

The next level of interoperability is the ability to share information at the data level, not just facilitate consistent environments, or the ability to "read" each other's data format. "Users should be able to get the correct information to the correct place when it is needed. Shared functions are also crucial. Changes made at the system level by one tool should be back-annotated and highlighted at the subsystem level by other tools."[12] For example, a wire in a 3D digital mock-up should be highlighted when selected as a circuit in a schematic. Or a PCB packaging should show changes to the PCB geometry based on changes being made at the devices level of a schematic design tool. In summary, different tools should function as operational extensions of each other.

6.6.2 Interdiscipline interoperability

Information can be exchanged between mechanical design packages. There are various levels of data transfer. Minimally a designer can transfer a bit-mapped image which can be used as part of a process instruction sheet or red-lined by fellow designers. This level of data transfer allows only one view of the data and contains no intelligence other than the image as presented.

Figure 6.4 shows the level of information exchange of the MCAD data process.

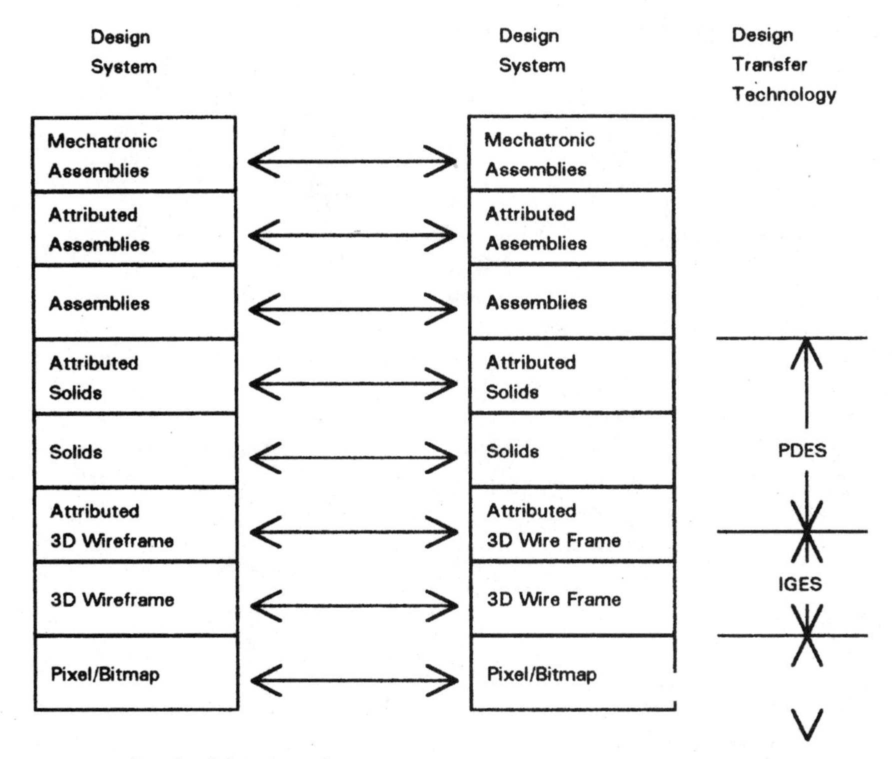

Figure 6.4 Levels of data transfer.

Moving up the data exchange ladder, basic wire frame geometry can be transferred via a data exchange protocol such as IGES. In this case the receiver of the information can actually manipulate the graphic information received such that he or she can see alternate views or actually change the design of the view itself.

There are several problems with the current technology. One is data mismatch. If an attributed 3D solid is converted to a bit-mapped image, which typically has no attributes, the receiver of this database will only be able to make limited design decisions. Typically the data should transferred horizontally instead of diagonally between the two design systems.

The second problem is that there is no means or standard for the communication of mechatronic designs across different systems. Larger CAD vendors may do this work in-house by trying to coordinate the geometric applications and representations of attributes between individual products; however, there are no standards. For example, consider a vendor that wants to do cabinet design which takes into account the heat given off by PCBs as well as motors. With a schematic in hand that feeds a PCB router the designer knows what components are used and has access to heat output information. This information in many cases can be sent to a CAD system for physical modeling. With any luck the heat characteristics of the chips on the PCB are carried with the location information of the PCB and its components. The designer will be even luckier if this 3D CAD model can then be sent through to a finite element thermal analysis of the PCB, motors, and heat dissipating equipment.

Each vendor mentioned in this section typically offers direct translation to a known standard such as PDES or can directly produce native database files such as AutoCad dxf files. There are, however, vendors that provide direct translators between various design tools. PDES/ STEP level exchange is coming to fruition. "Engineers from Ford have successfully transferred descriptive (3D models) for an automobile connecting rod to a Department of Energy facility."[13] This marks the first time that data transfer and machining has occurred under the Standard for the Exchange of Product Model Data (STEP) using different software programs. This is a key step to ensuring data between suppliers and customers can be effectively utilized vs. just shared.

6.7 Data Management

Most companies have had many years of experience with CAD tools. Many CAD drawings, schematics, and 3D models have been created. Additionally, there are other project-related data that are critical to the success of the project or program. These data include, but are not limited to, spreadsheets, word processing documents, NC toolpaths, and analyses results. The amount of data to manage is significant, and rapidly increasing as more companies turn to automation software to assist their development process. This is represented in Fig. 6.5. The need to manage the project data including drawings, models, schematics, spreadsheets, etc., will increase substantially with the explosion of data generated utilizing solid modeling, digital mock-ups, and finite element analysis. The data will be vector, raster, and text files all related to the project under development.

Data which are proliferated by the systems to produce digital mock-ups and schematics and perform finite analysis must be accurate and available to all personnel. These data include all part designs, logical schematics, printed circuit board layouts, NC tool paths, manufacturing sequences (exploded view drawings), user documentation, and service manuals. Software that is focused on managing data related to development, manufacturing, and service is an absolute must to

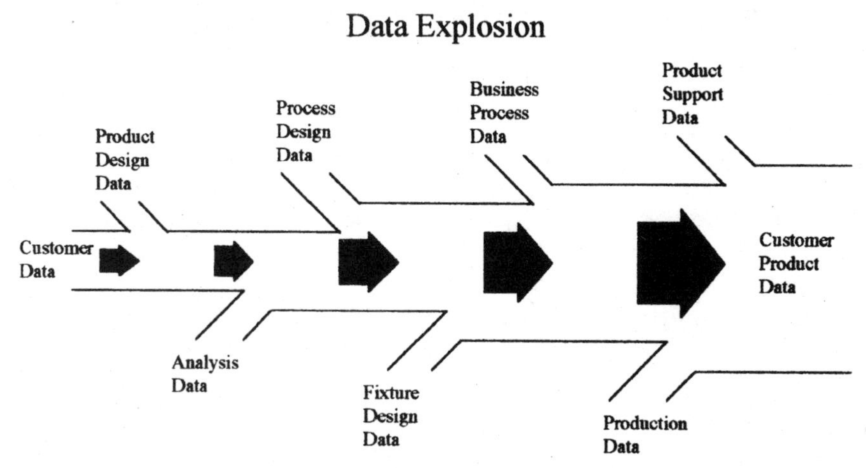

Figure 6.5 Data explosion.

improve the success of the development project. In a sense, a data management system is the "backbone" of mechatronics.

This is a mountain of data which has been revised tens, if not hundreds, of times. It is extremely critical that the most up-to-date revision of any of the data be accessible. The history of the revisions of the data must be kept and the configurations of manufactured units must be stored, to name some of the most important uses of the data. This mountain of data cannot be managed manually in a traditional paper vault. The data need to be managed electronically to ensure that those with proper access rights can access any bit of data, the most up-to-date revisions are shared with internal personnel and suppliers, backups of the data are made automatically on a periodic basis, review procedures are monitored, and approval procedures are conducted.

Additionally, longer life cycle products such as automobiles and especially aircraft require overhauls, upgrades, and periodic maintenance. These long-term requirements necessitate significant data retrieval and modification to ensure drawings are correct based on the latest revision. There may be literally hundreds of revisions for a particular product, such as passenger aircraft. All revisions need to be stored, not just the most current revision. These products must be serviced, demanding easy access to prints, service manuals, service documents, and parts lists. The data are spread across multiple disciplines. A database with a relational data structure is well suited to address these needs.

The data needs to be accessed by any one at any time and the integrity of the data must be maintained at all times. Furthermore, if multiple personnel access the same data file, all users of the file must be informed that there are multiple users and who the users are. There must be control over revising an existing file that may have multiple users accessing the file.

Enterprise data management software provides complete data security and project organization support for all company applications. The software stores, catalogs, and retrieves any type of data or graphic file, process plans, numerical control programs, and manufacturing and service data. Efficient sharing of accurate and up-to-date information focused on the product as a whole is a reality. Without it, achieving a mechatronic process is virtually impossible.

6.8 Role of CAE/CAD/CAM Suppliers

As previously discussed, engineering is a series of trade-offs. Whoever makes the best trade-offs in the shortest amount of time will likely have the best design. Today, designers analyze, evaluate, and simulate trade-offs with the help of computers. However, too many computer-aided design tools lock users into purely mechanical or electrical environments, impeding the ability to make trade-offs.

For mechatronics to become a reality, traditional CAD/CAM and EDA solutions must be integrated into a single environment. This does not imply that one database is required. However, heterogeneous tools, including electrical, mechanical, etc., packages, must be able to share information for development to manufacturing. By padding data among tools, designers can optimize trade-offs across disciplinary boundaries.

Simultaneous with the thrust to utilize 3D modeling techniques to design structure and enclosure components, electrical engineering personnel can be acquiring expertise to define system-level logic. This requires utilizing customer requirements to define logic needed for systems. At the system level, the engineers define how the subsystems and major components are to be interconnected using an interconnection diagram or wiring diagram.

Identifying system logic provides the basis for all the intelligence needed for 3D modeling of wires, cables, and harnesses. A consistent tool for the capture of system, board, and component-level logic is needed.

Presently, the majority of simulation performed is focused at component- and board-level analysis. This can be expanded to include system-level analysis. For example, an analysis could be performed to determine fault conditions of a particular circuit that may be comprised of several printed circuit boards, a power supply, and several switches. This entire circuit could be simulated under specific conditions and corrected prior to actually assembling the circuit. Once again problems could be prevented that are related to incorrect design.

The input criteria could be based on performance data or testing conditions such as hypot, specific load, or voltage drop. These conditions and the results of the simulation could be input to electrical testing equipment. The testing results could be compared against the simulation results for accuracy. Adjustments could be made in assembly and simulation criteria could be modified to reflect actual results. There would be a tightly coupled feedback loop between test and simulation to improve reliability and performance of systems.

There is much opportunity for CAD/CAM suppliers to improve their solutions to work interoperability with other company's solutions. The real objective is for these suppliers to focus on the fact that ultimately an end product must be manufactured. Therefore, functionality needs to be added so that each solution is a natural extension of another solution to solve the total system problem.

6.9 Hardware and Networks

Software applications of all types, once available only to a select few, primarily the engineering community, are now generally available to the masses. This has a dramatic effect on the development team, since each member has the ability to use a variety of software to expedite development. The CAD/CAM/CAE industry witnessed explosive growth over the past 15 years to service the needs of the engineering community. Much of the growth was facilitated by the availability of low-cost workstations and elaborate networks. In fact, these tools of the trade (hardware and networks) need to expand to facilitate more seamless information sharing among development team members, which include mechanical and electrical engineers that traditionally have been isolated from each other.

The evolution of hardware and networks connecting computer systems has been perverse. Not too long ago, most computer systems consisted of a host computer supporting a plethora of "dumb terminals" located throughout a development facility. This environment was made popular by IBM to support accounting systems, and eventually engineering systems. However, engineering groups were demanding more than the host-based system could provide, including easier use, computer-intensive applications (vs. transaction-based applications, such as accounting systems), and local security. Thus the PC and workstation environment was created to address these needs of the single engineer.

6.9.1 Hardware

Selecting the right PC or workstation configuration for the individual engineer or department of engineers is an important consideration. What is the necessary processing power required for the engineer? It depends on what applications will be used by the individual, how often the system will be utilized, and what is the price of the hardware to meet the needs. Processing power has been expanding rapidly over the past 10 years, while at the same time the price has been decreasing at a significant pace. Therefore, the unit cost per processing power has been decreasing exponentially. Many factors need to be considered when identifying a workstation or PC. Some of the considerations are listed in the following illustration.

Application requirements ultimately drive the necessity for a minimum amount of disk space. This disk space requirement must be satisfied before the system is even turned on. The need to configure the system with the appropriate size of disk to support the operating system and applications is an issue that the user faces before even using the application.

Once an engineer is using a particular application, performance becomes an immediate factor when working day in and out on a system. Performance, though determined to some extent by the bus interface to the disk itself, is most visibly affected by the amount of memory in the computer and the processing speed of the central processing unit. Figure 6.6 shows the relationship between processor speed, memory, and overall system performance. For each particular microprocessor

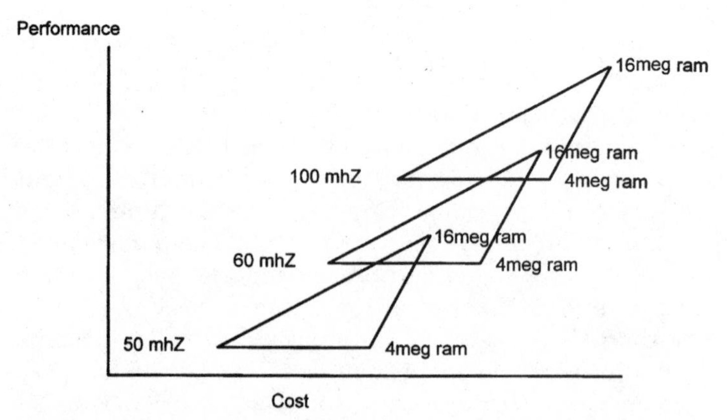

Figure 6.6 Processor speed, memory, and overall system performance.

speed there is a performance triangle. As memory, which costs money, is added to the system the performance can be increased. The performance triangle of one microprocessor can actually overlap the performance triangle of a microprocessor, but at a lesser cost. Thus for a given dollar investment in many cases it makes more sense to buy a system with a lot of memory and then take the next step up in processor performance.

6.9.2 Networks

Another key issue that has emerged with the proliferation of PCs and workstations is to determine a method to share information quickly, inexpensively, and easily. Many PCs and workstations are in use by engineers on the development team to perform a variety of functions. With the power at the desktop, the amount of information that an engineer can generate is staggering. Furthermore, multiply the amount of information at the desktop of one engineer by the number of engineers in the organization, and the amount of information potentially available to all personnel is earth-shattering. Of course, it is imperative that this information be made available to all personnel. That has been a stumbling block. However, it has been addressed by most organizations. Some organizations have been more aggressive while other organizations have let individuals or departments address the issue.

Since most departments are organized along functional lines, such as mechanical engineering department, electrical engineering department, and so on, the first logical step for sharing information is to share the information locally, within the individual departments, using local area networks (LANs). An example of the typical layout of a LAN for a small engineering group is depicted in Fig. 6.7. It represents a typical network comprised of two ethernet segments connected by a repeater located in Building X. Each workstation or PC has local processing capabilities to perform functions on the installed software. This software could include CAD/CAM, CAE, PCB design, spreadsheet, word processing, and presentation software applications. In this example there are two servers. One server is providing communications and mass file storage support. The other server is providing support for printers and color plotters. These servers provide the capability to all workstations or PCs on the network that have the proper access rights.

Another trend which is important to understand is that software applications are generally focused on each of the departments or functional areas, and by and large, solutions are marketed to solve problems of the specific functional area. For example, PCB design

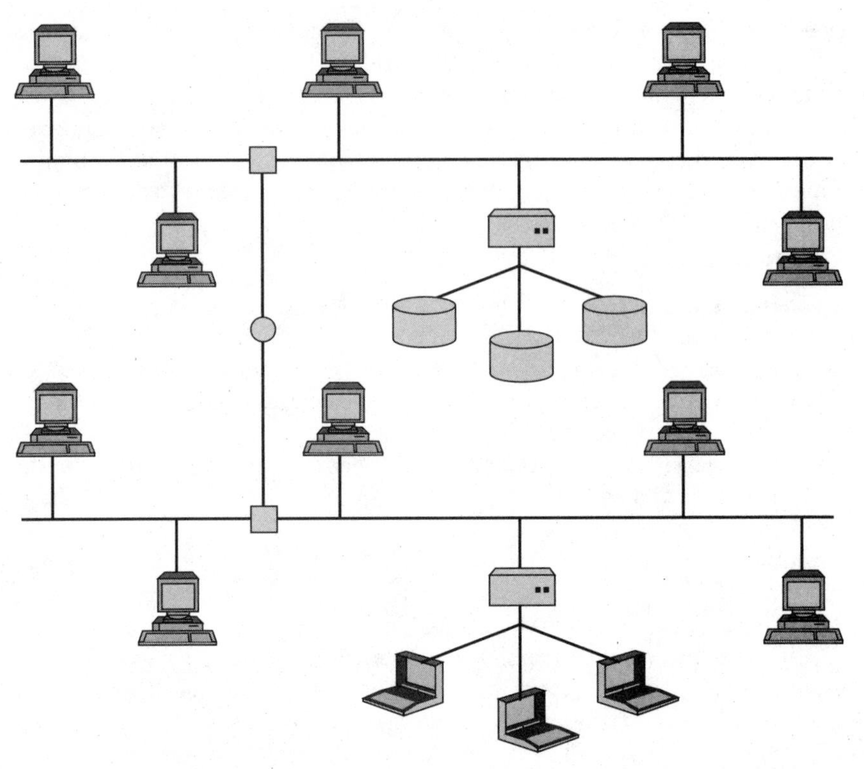

Figure 6.7 Typical layout of a LAN.

software packages are oriented to electrical engineers while geometric modeling and drafting software packages are targeted for mechanical engineers. This has the effect of separating the mechanical and engineering communities as each group interconnects its own PCs and workstations via the use of LANs. Many LANs have emerged within most companies which are primarily focused on one functional area. In fact, each functional area generally maintains the LAN. In some cases, the existence of a LAN may only be known by the group who created and is maintaining it. It becomes very difficult to share information among multiple functional areas when LANs are proliferated for the sole purpose of supporting one specific group.

It is clear that this technology provided the environment for small departments, housing specific disciplines, to expand their own capabilities, irrespective of other groups. The opportunity to become an island was made relatively easy by both the hardware and network technology, as well as the focus of the software suppliers on one specific group. Suppliers of software to assist the engineering community focused on either mechanical or electrical engineers. Most software companies continue to proliferate this separation with second- and third-generation software applications. However, a trend is emerging to focus on the entire product development using a system approach. This requires that mechanical and electrical engineers work in unison.

To yield a unified, cohesive environment, each of the groups needs to share information electronically and have software applications that consider both mechanical and electrical constraints throughout the product life cycle. The software requirements to consider mechanical and electrical requirements were previously addressed in this chapter. From a workstation, PC, and network perspective the most stringent requirement falls on the network to supply information across many groups that are located throughout a wide geographic area, perhaps the entire world. Absent of software applications, information sharing is extremely important so that each group can understand the needs of other groups. To meet this need to share in- formation between departments located in geographically different areas, wide area networks (WANs) emerged. An example of a simple WAN is shown in Fig. 6.8.

An entire world of information has been opened up to many engineers in different departments and the members of the development team because of WAN capabilities. For that matter, any team can have access to a plethora of information via wide area networks. The effect on development, where mechanical and electrical contraints can be identified and evaluated over the product life cycle early in development, is extremely positive. This is enabled by having the information available at any time to those personnel who have proper access rights to the information. Anyone anywhere in the world can gain easy access to information that may affect the development of a product. This is especially important to mechanical and electrical engineers who have LANs specific to their functional area. These LANs can be interconnected to provide the communication medium to share desperately needed information.

It is unrealistic to expect in today's global economy that the entire development, manufacturing, and service teams can all be physically colocated to meet the customer's product life cycle requirements. With the communications capabilities that exist today, the teams can be virtually colocated. A multiplicity of information can be created and shared anywhere. The software, hardware, and network technology is readily available for development teams to share this information early and often in the development cycle. The behavior to share information must be consistently reinforced, an organization structure focused on team involvement, and the technology provided to make mechatronics a reality.

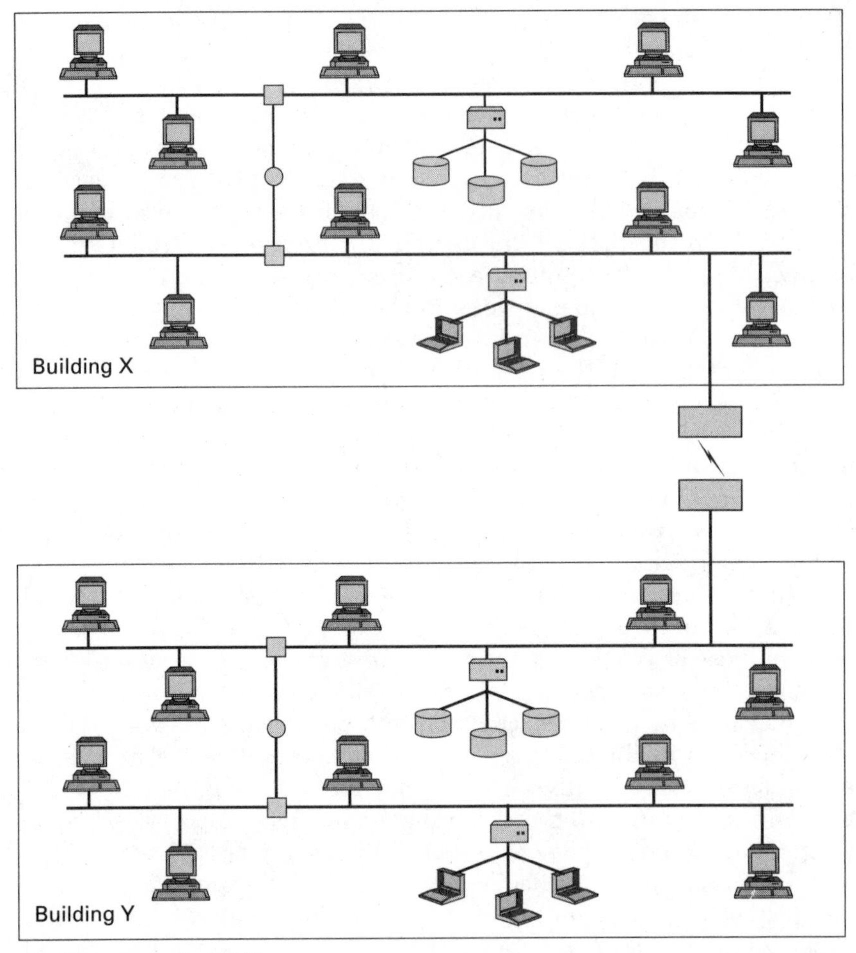

Figure 6.8 A simple WAN.

References

1. Wakely and Sharp: "Vehicle Wiring Harness Design at Land Rover," Computervision European User's Group Conference, April 1989.
2. Tomkinson, Donald: "Getting MEs and EEs to Work in Harmony," *Machine Design,* Jan. 23, 1992, p. 64.
3. Computervision: "From Wood and Canvas to World Class," *Contact,* Summer 1992, p. 5.
4. Gottschalk, Mark A.: "How Boeing Got to 777th Heaven," *Design News,* Sept. 12, 1994, p. 50.
5. King, Russell: "Chrysler's Cirrus Carves New Niche," *Design News,* Oct. 10, 1994, p. 29.
6. Computervision: "From Wood and Canvas to World Class," *Contact,* Summer 1992, p. 6.

7. Gottschalk, Mark A.: "How Boeing Got to 777th Heaven," *Design News,* Sept. 12, 1994, p. 51.
8. Tomkinson, Donald: "Getting MEs and EEs to Work in Harmony," *Machine Design,* Jan. 23, 1992, p. 62.
9. Puttre, Michael: "Putting Optimization Routines in the Loop," *Mechanical Engineering,* July 1993, p. 77.
10. Teresko, John: "Service Now a Design Element," *Industry Week,* Feb. 7, 1994.
11. Constance, Joseph: "DFMA: Learning to Design for Manufacture and Assembly," *Mechanical Engineering,* May 1992, p. 70.
12. Boes, Bruce: "Implementing Mechatronics; A Design Approach for Optimum Product Development," *ECN,* 1993.
13. Murray, Charles J.: "Ford, DOE Collaborate on Product Data Transfer," *Design News,* Oct. 10, 1994, p. 49.

Chapter

7

Implementing a Mechatronic Process

It is important to understand the mechatronic process—how today's products require procedures which will optimize development and what software tools will facilitate a mechatronic approach. This is essentially the technology portion of the equation. Earlier in the book, the organization required to achieve a mechatronic approach was discussed. Unfortunately, technology and people alone will not achieve a mechatronic process. It must be properly implemented in a systematic manner. An organization needs to be flexible in the implementation, since no two organizations are the same. However, a set of guidelines can be used to implement a mechatronic approach. Implementation is the key to success. In fact, the technology or the theory of mechatronics is basically worthless without proper implementation.

With that in mind, the following discussion focuses on the guidelines which an organization, that wants to implement a mechatronic approach, can use. These are not rules, but a suggested methodology that each organization needs to modify to achieve a mechatronic approach. These guidelines are flexible enough to enable each organization to modify for its own needs, yet they provide the foundation so that everything is not done by exception. More importantly, a mechatronic approach is not something that can be achieved overnight. It requires many years of effort to achieve for most organizations because a cultural change is needed. Even more important is the fact that once a mechatronic process is achieved, it can always be improved. And thus continuous improvement becomes very important to the overall implementation.

In addition to the software tools that facilitate and automate a mechatronic process, there is a specific formalized method that can be used to help implement a mechatronic process, or any process for that matter. These methods range from assessment to process mapping which can be used to help identify the flow of the existing and envisioned or mechatronic process. These methods can also be used to help identify what software is presently being used and how to implement additional automation. It is easy to understand why implementing a mechatronic process takes time, but the time is worth the effort because of the immense benefits which can be realized. The benefits are discussed in the next chapter.

Like implementing other changes of this magnitude, such as total quality management, significant focus from top management is an absolute must. This commitment cannot be understated or trivialized. This commitment must flow through the entire organization to achieve a process that is long-lasting, performed in the shortest possible time, with a minimal amount of conflict. Conflict is generally prevalent when top management commitment is questionable and the need to implement changes is not a priority.

7.1 The Change Process

The procedure to achieve a mechatronic approach is fairly standard. The process consists of five main steps as shown in Fig. 7.1.

7.1.1 Decide to improve

The decision to improve may seem like a trivial subject. However, it is paramount to the success of any endeavor. When a company determines it must put in place mechanisms to foster improvement, it has taken the difficult first step to yield improvement. All organizations need to improve, or they will perish. This is especially true in today's global market, as competitors can arise anywhere in the world. In many cases the rise of a new competitor may not be clearly visible by existing manufacturers. It therefore becomes necessary to continuously improve.

Many companies have spent great energy to create a culture based on improvement as the cornerstone for future success. Others have sat idly by trying to decide if they need improvements. After all, they may have 60 percent market share, and it seems that no competitor will challenge that supremacy any time soon. This is very shortsighted. A company cannot afford to sit and react to competitive threats, because the reaction time may be too long to make a difference. The company needs to have the mentality to create a culture or process that requires continuous improvement. It also means the job of improving is a never-ending one. Once certain goals and objectives are

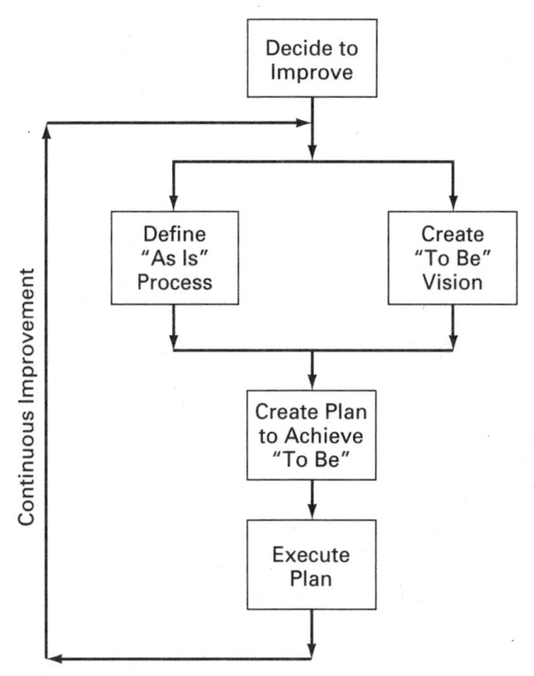

Figure 7.1 The five main steps to achieve a mechatronic approach.

met, new goals need to be established for the company to thrive. The process never ends.

Companies that have not ingrained continuous improvement into the culture need to begin this process immediately. Once an organization decides to improve, implementing the change can begin. Two main activities need to take place:

Identify the "As Is" process.

Determine the "To Be" process, or desired process.

Depending on the organization, the As Is process could be identified first and the To Be process determined next. In other companies it may be better to determine the To Be process first and the As Is process second. In most cases they are done somewhat in parallel if the existing process is not well known and the company is embarking on continuous improvement for the first time. The real key is to decide on what the optimum or desired process is. This can be determined by looking at the existing process and defining weaknesses or areas of opportunity or by wiping the slate clean and identifying the new or desired process.

Unfortunately, the two topics cannot be described in parallel. They must be discussed in sequence. In this case the As Is activity is discussed first and the To Be activity second. The sequence does not in any way construe that one precedes the other.

7.1.2 Identify the As Is process

The present process that a manufacturer is using to develop products is termed the As Is process. The existing process may be formalized or it may be ad hoc. In most cases the existing process is a combination of formalized and ad hoc procedures. The objective to improve requires that the existing process be formally recorded. Each step of the process needs to be identified, the relationship to other steps quantified, and the group responsible for the specific step determined. It may be beneficial for the manufacturer to utilize a consultant to help identify the process that is being used to develop products. The advantage of using an outside independent company to assist the assessment of the existing process is that hidden steps are uncovered, and thus an accurate picture of the existing process results.

A primary tool which is tremendously helpful to identify the existing process is cross-functional process mapping. These maps of process flows "describe the functions involved at each step of a particular process within the company."[1] The technique focuses on the processes and procedures which are key to the organization, in this case the product development process. An example of an As Is process is shown in Fig. 7.2. The basic elegance of these charts "is that they use only a few symbols and techniques to present a complex system or operation graphically."[2]

The team which develops the process maps needs to be a multifunctional team consisting of mechanical, electrical, and software engineers, as well as manufacturing and service representatives. The team should consist of "doers," not upper-level management, because these employees offer valuable insight into the daily business operations.[1] To help facilitate the team to accomplish its objective, an outside facilitator is recommended to work with this group. Motorola believes "an objective outsider is more likely to identify and challenge any bureaucracy within the organization."[1] A facilitator forces a company representative to defend the significance of each operation. The organization must provide the rationale for every step of the process, and the team soon discovers, by their own admission, which steps are no longer necessary. An accurate and complete description of the existing process results due to process mapping. This is key because this becomes the starting point to identify changes to yield the To Be or proposed process. In this particular case, the proposed process is a mechatronic process.

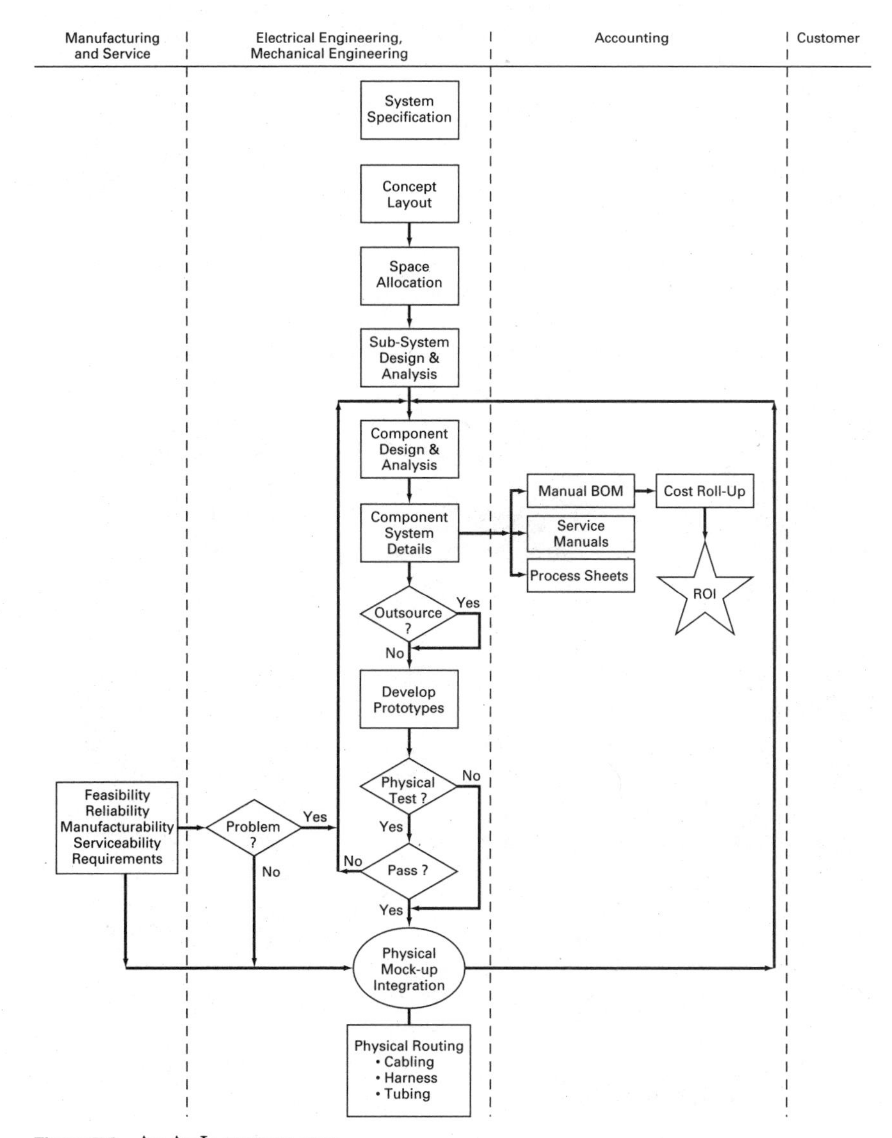

Figure 7.2 An As Is process map.

There are two other important parts of preparing the process maps. While identifying steps of the process, the group who performs the step needs to be identified. Additionally, the time it takes to complete the step of the process should be identified. In some cases a step may be required only a portion of the time. If this is the case, it is important to identify the approximate percentage of time the step occurs.

The process map is now complete, including the steps performed as part of the development process, the person or group that performs the step, the time it takes to complete the step, and the percentage of time a step is performed.

Another critical piece of the As Is process is to determine the computer systems that are presently being used. The team needs to identify the specifics of the installed computer systems such as what data are housed in what database and what is the format of the data, for example, what is the format of the part number, serial numbers, revision levels of the products, customer name, customer address, to list but a few. The To Be process will address computer requirements, and it is important to know the existing systems in order to determine the effort to get to the desired information system.

Next, the team needs to identify the steps that are redundant, do not add value, take too long to complete, or are performed by the incorrect group. The process map helps the team to easily identify each of these problems. These problems ultimately provide the opportunity to improve the process. In most cases it is important to prioritize the importance of the problems and resulting opportunities to help direct the team where to focus their efforts.

Sometimes to identify non-value-added steps the team needs to consider other proposed methods than the existing methods. A comparision to the To Be process is often helpful. Obviously, to implement a mechatronic process those steps in the existing process which will not help achieve the mechatronic process need to be eliminated.

An important benefit of this step, and a reason it is key to implementing a mechatronic process, is that the members of the multifunctional team obviously have to work together to create the process map. A by-product of this effort is that team members develop a better understanding of each other's problems, issues, and constraints. This is especially important for the mechatronic process, since mechanical engineers get the opportunity to understand the issues and constraints that electrical engineers must deal with during the product development process and vice versa.

7.1.3 Describe the To Be process

In the reengineering process, the To Be vision is identified next. This is the vision of the company or team. It is the process that, ultimately, the company wants or needs to achieve. The To Be process, in this case, is the mechatronic process that has been detailed throughout this book. It is important to note that the vision includes the mechatronic process and the tools which facilitate the process including mechanical and electrical CAD/CAM software solutions, data management, DFMA, and DFS solutions.

To create the To Be process it is beneficial to observe other companies within the same industry and among other industries to review the processes they may have in place to address a specific issue, such as product development or manufacturing capabilities. This is referred to as benchmarking. It is a very useful tool to help increase competitiveness in a variety of areas, including the product development process.

Process mapping is also a very valuable tool at this step. It is used to map and identify the proposed process. The proposed product development process needs to be identified by a cross-functional team. Additionally, consultants can be employed to help create the To Be vision. This vision may take many years to achieve, but nonetheless it is critical that the process is well defined so that specific steps to achieve the vision can be easily identified. An example of the To Be process follows for reference. In this case the identified process is the development process utilizing a digital mock-up vs. a physical mock-up process identified in an earlier illustration. Throughout the entire To Be process, as illustrated in Fig. 7.3, mechanical and electrical engineers must be working jointly if a mechatronic approach is to be a reality.

In most cases, the To Be process will entail definition of supporting computer or information systems. These systems are required to meet the To Be vision. The specific information and data, their format, and what databases will be used need to be identified as part of the To Be vision. Relative to the mechatronic process vision, critical information systems include CAD/CAM, CAE, DFMA, and DFS systems. As shown above, these systems are centered around creation and management of the digital mock-up.

7.1.4 Create a plan to achieve the mechatronic process

Once the As Is and To Be states are well defined, the next step is to create a plan to achieve the To Be state. An important part of this process is to determine the amount of gap between the As Is and the To Be states. This is often referred to as gap analysis. Figure 7.4 defines pictorially what a gap analysis is.

At this stage the real opportunities for improvement are quantified and the effort to achieve the desired process becomes defined because the gap is determined. During the analysis it is important to realize that some assumptions may be required; however, the team performing the analysis needs to quantify as much as possible the gap and what will be required to achieve the desired state. Also equally important is the fact that achieving the desired state will most likely require one or more phases. The specific parts of the gap analysis, or conclusions of the analysis, need to be prioritized in order to define what the team should work on first, second, third, etc. This prioritiza-

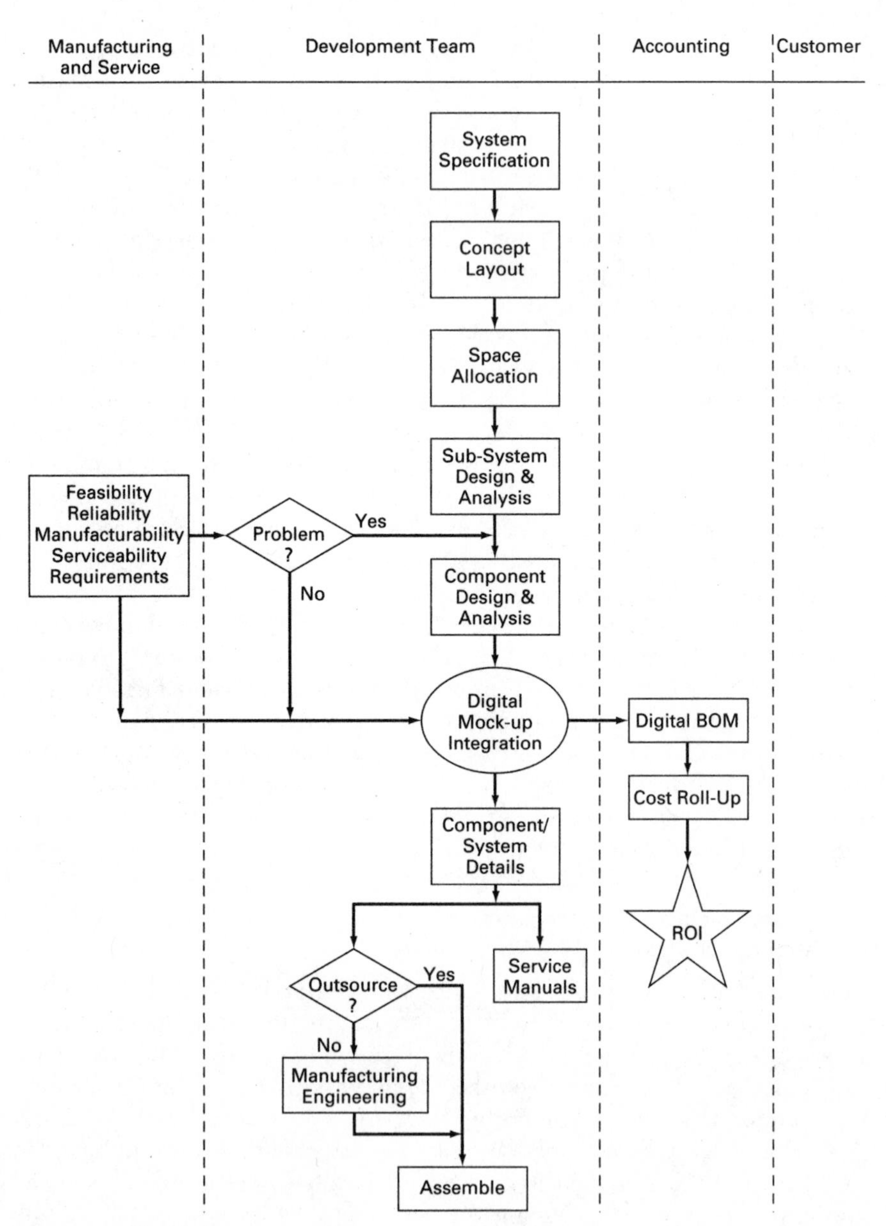

Figure 7.3 The To Be process map.

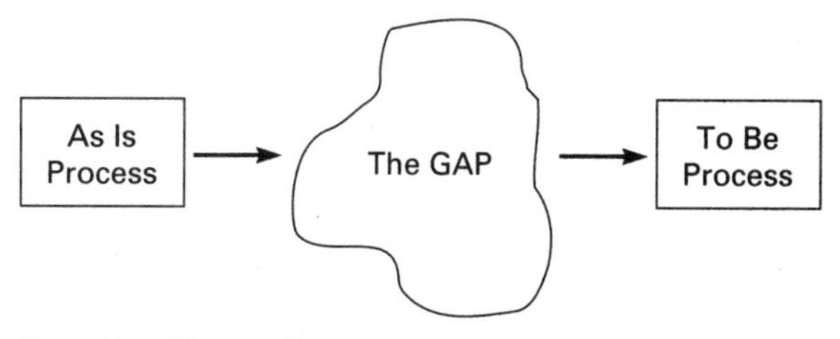

Figure 7.4 Gap analysis.

tion needs to be based on what factors will most affect the achievement of the desired process, in this case a mechatronic process.

To identify the specific steps to get to the To Be process and achieve a mechatronic process is not easy—hence the need for a detailed plan to convert the company's product development process to a mechatronic approach. Identifying and scheduling activities need to be accomplished with a cross-functional team consisting of mechanical, electrical, manufacturing, and service representatives. It is important to remember that the process that is determined will become the process that will be utilized for all product development. Achieving this capability is critically important to the success of the company.

As stated, the important task of this step is to identify the activities required to get from the existing process to the desired process in an orderly process which has many milestones. The group needs to focus on people, process, and technology. The specific analysis needs to be focused on people, process, and technology. All these criteria have been explored in detail in this book. Each of these major areas can be broken into many subsections which need to be evaluated to quantify "the gap." The people part of the equation refers mainly to the organization structure issues required to achieve a mechatronic process. Process refers to the detailed procedures and methodology that is the mechatronic process itself, and technology refers to the computer-aided tools such as CAC/CAM, CAE, data management, DFMA, and DFS that increase the ability to achieve a mechatronic approach.

The first key step is to create an organization that supports a mechatronic process. This requires a focus on the end product and a team consisting of mechanical, electrical, and software engineers, generally managed by a program or project manager. The team also should include representation from manufacturing and service. This can be done for all products or focused first on one or two projects at a time. The method will be predicated on the culture and inner workings of the organization.

The second step entails adding data management capabilities before mountains of electronic data become the norm. This enables the company to build the foundation prior to adding significant automation. The other key feature of this step is that most of the electronic data which is already being generated can be stored and managed. In most companies, there is some existing level of automation. It may be only 2D drawings of mechanical components and electrical schematics. More sophisticated tools may be in use, providing all the more reason to conduct this step early in the planned implementation.

The third step is to automate the mechatronic process starting with schematic capture and 3D modeling tools. The step has multiple substeps to ultimately achieve a fully automated process. This is the step to further automate each of the important disciplines, mechanical and electrical engineering. The next activity in the automation process is to utilize analysis and simulation capabilities to help optimize the design using software tools, as opposed to functionally testing prototypes. Finally, the last activity, within the automation step, is to reduce and ultimately eliminate all physical mock-ups and testing prototypes, through the use of digital mock-ups. These mock-ups contain all the components and assemblies including structural, exterior package, printed circuit boards, and wires. The digital mock-up is the master for all other operations. It is also the medium for communication among development team members.

Based on the above defined step, a specific schedule can be determined which details what is needed, who is responsible for conducting the tasks, and when a task or activity will be completed. This definition is typical project definition and management. Several tools are available to assist project management, including Gantt charts, CPM (critical path method), and project management software. All these tools are used to define, prioritize, schedule, and track progress. It is best when this plan contains many well-defined small steps to achieve the desired process. The reason for small steps is that success is best measured in small steps. Momentum is easier to maintain when milestones can be reached with reasonable effort, not monumental effort. When a milestone is reached, success needs to be published to leverage these small achievements to continue to press for the ultimate achievement, the implementation of a mechatronic process.

Selecting a vendor or consultant. A key to any plan to implement a process change of this magnitude is to select the correct software supplier and, if used, the right consultant. Actually, as briefly discussed earlier, the use of a consultant to help determine the As Is process can be very advantageous owing to the unbiased view of a third party. It is recommended that this consultant be employed in the remaining stages of the change process including helping to create and map the To Be process, to identify an implementation plan, and to execute the plan.

How does an organization select a consultant who can assist the change process? The emphasis is on assisting the process. The consultant should help facilitate the process, to work with the cross-functional team, not replace the team. The team must lead the endeavor, and top management cannot be led to think that the consultant can do the entire activity. It is very unlikely that the change will be fully implemented without ownership and responsibility being borne by representatives of the company. Cosmetic changes can occur without maximum organizational commitment and activity.

Some of the key guidelines an organization can use to select a consultant to assist the change process:

- *Product development process experience.* Find a consultant who has experience modifying product development processes of many companies in a variety of industries. A key is that the person or persons need to have had exposure to assisting companies that have electrical and mechanical components and assemblies. The reason for a variety of industries centers around the ability to be exposed to various methods that might be specific to a certain industry. Multiple industries would lead to a benchmarking methodology, as previously discussed.
- *References.* Related to the first item is the references that a consultant has. What is most important is the goals as defined, the measurements identified to determine the success of the recommendations, and the results. Results which should be measured include shorter development time, number of personnel and cost to develop products, and product life cycle costs as compared to previous products developed prior to the introduction of the modified process. If any of these are missing, the organization may be taking a risk with the consultant to achieve desired results.
- *Independence.* It is critical that the consultant not be employed by companies such as software or hardware companies which could gain by the consultant's recommendations. Additionally, all alliances, both formally and informally, need to be completely understood to ensure the recommendations are as unbiased as possible.
- *Documentation.* A consultant needs to have the capabilities to provide superior documentation for the processes that exist and the proposed processes. This documentation needs to include a clear definition of the milestones and items the consultant will deliver to achieve the desired process. The consultant needs to provide examples of the documentation. It is also critical that this documentation be easy to understand for those members of the team charged with the task of changing the development process.

The selection of the correct consultant will go a long way to accelerating the achievement of a product development process based on a mechatronic approach. Conversely, the selection of an incorrect consultant not only could slow the change process but may even may lead to the incorrect process that is worse than the existing process. The effects on competitiveness if this happens are apparent. Hence the organization must be totally involved in the change process, using the consultant to facilitate the process, to help determine recommendations, to create an implementation plan, and to define measurements to gauge the success of the new process.

Another key area for the organization to keep in mind is the selection of computer software and hardware vendors, or partners. The timing of their involvement can be critical. Early involvement obviously supports the creation of achievable recommendations and plans. However, their involvement at early stages must be monitored closely to ensure the vendor does not bias the recommendations to the benefit of the supplier. Creating recommendations at generic level such as functions required, not specific company software packages, is most advantageous. An example would be the recommendation to use digital mock-ups to replace the use of physical mock-ups. A poor recommendation would be to specify software for solid modeling from a certain company. This comes later after the To Be process has been formulated, as part of the implementation plan when specific software packages need to be evaluated. The objective is to select software packages will lead to the achievement of the recommendation, based on cost and capabilities.

Many criteria can be used to select the correct software vendor. The hardware can be selected after the software, since most software can be used on a variety of industry leading platforms. This is due in large part to the open systems architecture employed by today's leading computer hardware suppliers. Some of the major items to consider when selecting a software supplier include:

- *Open architecture.* Do the systems to be employed have an open architecture such that other applications can be easily integrated to create the total solution? It is virtually impossible that one company can provide the total solution for product development, accounting, manufacturing, and customer service. The key then becomes to easily integrate these systems together to create the total solution, which will take several steps to fully implement. Additionally, can the new system work with existing systems? Can the legacy data which reside in the existing databases be easily migrated forward to the new database?

- *User environment.* Does the software have a user environment that is easy to use by most of the personnel including frequent and casual users? The interface must have minimal steps to select a desired operation. The information needs to be easy for the user to find in the shortest time possible. Are there on-line help facilities to assist the user to achieve the desired results?
- *Company stability.* Will the vendor be around next year? Most implementations take several years to complete, so it is important to ensure the vendor will have financial health during the implementation period. It is important not just to be in existence, but to be expanding capabilities and attracting new customers. It is recommended that the organization use standard financial reports, such as Dun and Bradstreet, as well as annual reports and business plans.
- *Integrity.* Is the vendor consistent, honest, fair, and faithful? Old-fashioned business integrity is a key ingredient. These are achieved over time and by the vendor's experience base. Many system deficiencies can be overlooked if the vendor is faithful to its business dealings and the defined intent of the working arrangement. It is almost impossible to ensure items are covered prior to creation of the implementation plan, no matter what experience the vendor may have. There are just too many unknowns and the environment is too dynamic. Much of this information can be garnered by speaking to a variety of the vendor's customers.
- *Strategy.* What is the vendor's long-range (3- to 5-year) plan? It is critical to understand the vendor's long-range plans prior to entering a long-term agreement. As much as possible it is important whose goals and objectives coincide with the organization implementing the change.
- *Implementation assistance.* What assistance does the vendor provide to ensure the success of the implementation? Does it include planning assistance, installation and setup, training, customization, and ongoing assistance? It can be expected that these are value-added services; however, they should not be minimized if the organization expects the implementation to be successful. All documentation to support the implementation needs to be made available, especially training and documentation for any customizations conducted. Last, support during a pilot phase and early crossover to production is very critical to the success of the entire implementation. In fact, it is advised that all payments to the vendor should be contingent upon the successful (as determined by the customer) completion of milestones staggered throughout the implementa-

tion. The organization needs to ensure that the vendor is committed to success of the implementation, and this is where the rubber meets the road. As stated earlier, technology without implementation is basically worthless.

- *User group.* Does the vendor have an active user group conducted by the users, not the vendor? These groups are invaluable for providing information to the organization implementing software to support the reengineering of the product development process. This group needs to be tapped for all information as it relates to the vendor including reputation and software use assistance, and as a method to prioritize the vendor's future development.

7.1.5 Execute the plan

It may seem that, with all the preparation described above, executing the plan would be a straightforward, trivial process. Unfortunately, that is not the case. In fact, this is the most difficult and frustrating part of the process. There is no doubting the fact that proper and extensive preparation will significantly reduce the risk of implementation, as many of the issues that may arise should be considered as part of the implementation plan. The experience factor will have a great deal of effect on being able to identify and consider a multitude of implementation issues that will arise. However, it is not possible to consider all issues that may arise, and quite frankly, the team can't take time to consider all issues. Why? It will delay the execution of the implementation without significant risk reduction. A tough and sometimes gut-wrenching decision to proceed must be made as soon as practical. That decision needs to be made by the team, with the assistance of the consultant (if employed).

Frustration is often rampant because reengineering the development process based on a mechatronic approach is being conducted in parallel with existing duties. This is true for most reengineering efforts. Duties existed prior to the implementation for all the team members. It is crucial, if at all possible, to have a core of team members devoted to the change process, supported by a larger group performing their existing tasks as well as assisting the implementation.

All resources needed to execute the implementation need to be made available to complete the plan. A program manager or project manager needs to be selected who can execute the plan. The person should have experience in executing programs of this size and complexity. The program or project manager continuously needs to track the progress against the original plan, and adjust the plan and schedule accordingly. This may be required only for a particular product development because the organization may have elected to implement the process on one product first before expanding to all subsequent product development projects.

Once execution of the implementation plan begins, there is generally no turning back. That does not mean there is no flexibility to alter or modify the plan as the implementation plan is executed. In fact, flexibility is the key to success, since many issues that were not envisioned will inevitably arise. The team must be able to respond quickly to new information and issues and adjust the plan accordingly. As milestones are reached (and there should be many well-identified milestones in the plan), it is important to publish success to the organization to build momentum and acceptance. Ultimately, momentum used properly will accelerate the execution of the plan as people jump on the bandwagon.

Another key issue affecting the inability to turn back centers around the fact that, in most cases, new computer software and hardware is being implemented. Obviously, to return to the previous environment is virtually impossible. Having both the old and new for any period of time except the transition period is prohibitively costly. The system costs and personnel costs are doubled, and therefore unacceptable. Again, this does not mean the team's hands are tied. In any implementation, it is critically important that a backup solution should be identified in the event the computer software and hardware that is part of the implementation plan is not working as planned.

7.1.6 Continuous improvement

Upon the achievement of a mechatronic approach throughout the organization, the implementation of continuous improvement needs to take place. This step, as shown in the change process illustration, is never-ending. There will always be parts of the process that can be improved, especially new technology which will become available to facilitate the mechatronic process. Additionally, the product content will evolve as customers demand more functionality of a given product or demand functionality which leads to an entirely new product. The organization must set up an ongoing process to strive for continuous improvement. This is usually accomplished using teams which focus on various areas to improve. The first objective is to understand all the specific areas that can be improved, prioritize the list, and select the most important issue to address first.

A method to assist the team is for the team to think about how to make the process faster, better, and cheaper. Another method is to evaluate where on the integration continuum the organization falls. Figure 7.5 is an illustration of the continuum. Going from left to right

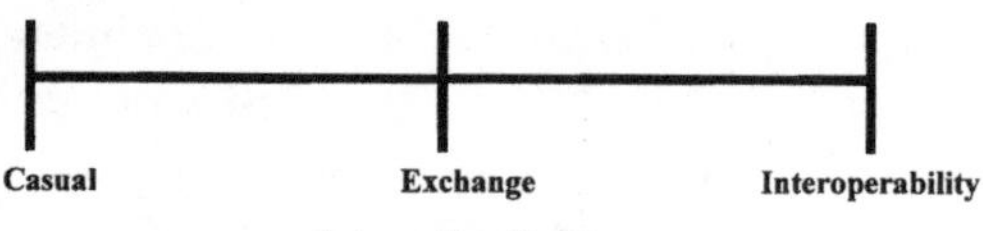

Figure 7.5 The integration continuum.

the organization has increased integration capabilities, ultimately achieving interoperability.

There are general characteristics associated with each level of the integration continuum. An organization can fall anywhere on the continuum. The status of integration is not restricted to only the three levels; it can be a combination of two or more levels. A casual integration capability is characterized by "windows" of inconsistent user interface operations, the need to reenter data because of incompatibility of systems, required access of multiple systems, data sharing between windows, user need to facilitate the movement of data, and a consistent way to access data. The next level, exchange, is characterized by the ability to share information across the interface without manual intervention, a consistent user environment, automated standards for data exchange, access to multiple systems and platforms, data sharing directly between applications, and network communication facilities with data dictionaries used. Presently, the highest level, termed interoperability, can be characterized by a single view with a consistent user interface of all information, all information automatically managed across heterogeneous platforms, and all information treated with a common approach. It is important to note that the highest level is a snapshot in time and will change as technology advances.

With all these reference points, the team needs to identify improvements on a continual basis. Once an issue has been identified which needs improvement, the team needs to recommend methods to improve the issue and implement improvements to the then current process. And then the cycle repeats itself into infinity.

The importance of the continuous improvement step cannot be understated. Achieving a mechatronic process is the primary goal; however, its achievement alone will not sustain a competitive advantage that may have resulted. To increase the chance of maintaining a competitive advantage, a company needs to continuously improve.

References

1. Angelucci, George: "Cycle-Time Reduction: A Minute Saved Is a Minute Earned," *AFSM International,* April 1994, p. 29.
2. Shina, Sammy G.: "Concurrent Engineering," *IEEE Spectrum,* July 1991, p. 26.

Chapter

8

Conclusion

Today's manufacturers are faced with a plethora of issues, pressures, and obstacles that they must weed through to be successful. Increasingly markets are becoming more global. This includes opportunities present with more markets that may have been previously unattainable for the manufacturer. There is more opportunity then ever to sell products to untapped markets. However, a global economy also translates to increased competition as markets become less protected. Competition can now come from companies halfway around the world, from sources that were never possible only a few years ago. These trends will not abate. More and more markets will become available as the worldwide standard of living increases. More and more companies will be competing in the existing and expanded marketplace.

Manufacturers cannot stand still for a moment. They need to be able to quickly and adeptly identify, develop, manufacture, distribute, and service products for the global economy. They need to have a formalized process which assists in identifying, developing, manufacturing, distributing, and servicing of products. This cannot be left to chance.

Manufacturers are responding to customer requirements for new functionality in all products by utilizing a significant quantity of electronics in an aesthetically pleasing and ergonomic package. The growth of electrical and electronic content of nearly all products is exploding at a exponential pace in an attempt to meet this thirst for extra functionality that consumers are demanding. The rate of adding functions to products does not appear to be diminishing, and in fact, the growth will probably accelerate as technological advances take place.

There is significant opportunity to increase the success of the product development process, using a mechatronic approach, for almost any type of product developed and manufactured today because nearly all products combine electrical, mechanical, and software content. Most of the technology, via the use of hardware and software, is readily available to facilitate the improvement of the product development process based on a mechatronic approach. The procedure to achieve a mechatronic process is not a secret. It is not some untried method where a company may be risking its future by implementing such a methodology. Quite the opposite is true. Those companies who develop, manufacture, and service products with electrical and mechanical content, who don't implement a mechatronic approach, are risking their future. Furthermore, the journey does not end with the achievement of a mechatronic approach being used. It has just begun because the process needs to be continuously improved to remain competitive.

Many manufacturers in a variety of industries have already implemented a mechatronic process. A train manufacturer squeezed considerable electronics and wiring into a minimum space on a recently developed engine. Everything assembled together on the first try because a mechatronic approach was employed.[1] A manufacturer of HVAC access and security controls has its mechanical and electrical engineers working more closely. Engineers are more sensitive to each other's constraints. Electrical engineers consider fits and clearances while mechanical engineers are beginning to understand that they need to determine enclosure size based on the electronics capabilities that must be housed. As a result, the firm has reduced lead times by more than 50 percent over the past 5 years. It has also doubled engineering output by cutting the staff by one-third.[1]

Emphasis on product development process based on a mechatronic approach, like quality programs, needs to be an integral part of corporate thinking and organizational structure. Otherwise the tools, training, and effort will not yield the desired results. Top management needs to be committed to implementing a mechatronic approach. Engineers and company personnel need to be focused on the goal of developing the end product, not just their respective components or subassemblies for which they have direct responsibility. A total system focus is required of everyone. Reorganizations may be required to align the personnel properly. One firm that has successfully reorganized to yield a mechatronic approach is a leader in fuel, speed, and torque systems. Previously they were organized by function like many firms. Now multidisciplined operating groups comprising electrical, mechanical, and manufacturing engineers concentrate on specific end markets. Workers become more efficient when they focus on a particular product line rather than juggling projects slated for different markets.[2]

Achieving a mechatronic approach to product development takes a lot of time and effort. It does not happen overnight. A sustained effort is required to achieve a new process that breaks many cultural barriers that may have existed for decades. In the past, electrical and mechanical engineers have not worked in a cooperative and team environment. They have worked well among each of their respective disciplines but not across disciplines. This separatism started well before the mechanical and electrical engineers entered the workforce. It started at the college level.

The implementation of a product development process based on a mechatronic approach requires change, and therefore change management. Change needs to be phased in using well-defined bite-size steps. This requires multiple milestones through the implementation plan. When a milestone is reached, it needs to be published to help maintain momentum and ensure that achieving a mechatronic process is a reality. A leading car manufacturer recognized that implementing a mechatronic approach takes time. They are applying mechatronics methodology across all designs, while at the same time they are upgrading their automation tools gradually. In the first stage, logic design and structural design groups are being automated. In the second stage, designers will prepare digital mock-ups that include structural, electrical, and electronic components.[2] In the final stage, the entire process will be integrated together with the focus on the end product. Then continuous improvement methods will be employed to evolve the process.

All the hard work is worth the effort. The benefits associated with achieving a mechatronic process outweigh the risks. Although the need for mechatronics increases with design complexity, the benefits apply to manufacturers at all levels of the product hierarchy, including manufacturers of subsystems, assemblies, and components. In fact, a mechatronic approach is required at lower levels to ensure that products fit together and work as expected. At the subsystems level contents include electrical and mechanical components, so the need for a mechatronic approach cannot be overstated. Since the components and subsystems are ultimately assembled together to yield an end product, it stands to reason that a mechatronic approach is needed. In effect the end product is only as good as its components, and "mechatronics must be built in," similar to quality.

Some of the key benefits of implementing a product development process based on a mechatronic approach include shorter time to market, increased quality and reliability, and reduced development, manufacturing, and service costs. Average maintenance times have decreased because service departments can now access mechanical and electrical engineering data.

Ultimately, an organization's competitiveness is greatly increased. The ability to bring products to market that meet the needs of the global community yields a distinctive competitive advantage for the manufacturer. However, the manufacturer cannot rest on its laurels for any period of time. The company must continuously strive to improve its development processes. If it does not, the competitive advantage will evaporate in a very short period of time.

Having the right automation tools, such as CAD/CAM, data management software, and DFMA software, does not guarantee that a mechatronic approach has been achieved. It does not guarantee success. Neither does a corporate reorganization or a cross-training program for engineers. These are all important to the achievement and longevity of a mechatronic approach, but they need to be in balance. This balance varies for different companies. It is up to each company to identify a multidisciplined team to determine the right balance of tools, process, organization, and education. Those companies that achieve a balance will have a higher rate of success in achieving a mechatronic approach.

The question, therefore, is not if, but when? The time is now. It is quite clear that those companies who forge ahead and implement a product development process based on a mechatronic approach will be better poised for success in today's global economy.

References

1. Tomkinson, Donald: "Getting MEs and EEs to Work in Harmony," *Machine Design*, Jan. 23, 1994, p. 61.
2. Tomkinson, Donald: "Getting MEs and EEs to Work in Harmony," *Machine Design*, Jan. 23, 1994, p. 62.

Appendix

Universities Offering Mechatronics Programs

City Polytechnic of Hong Kong
Department of Manufacturing Engineering
Kowloon
Hong Kong

Colorado State University
Department of Mechanical Engineering
Fort Collins, CO

Concordia University
Centre for Industrial Control
Department of Mechanical Engineering
1455 de Maisonneuve Blvd. West
Montreal, Quebec H3G-1M8
Canada

Cranfield University
U.K.

Curtin University of Technology
Engineering and Science
GPO Box U1987
Perth
Western Australia 6001

Danish Technical University
Institute for Product Development
Institute for Engineering Design
Build 423
DK-2800 Lyngby
Denmark

Ecole Nationale Superieure de Mechanique et des Microtechniques
La bouloie
F-25030 Besançon
France

Georgia Institute of Technology
George Woodruff School of Mechanical Engineering
Atlanta, GA 30332

Gifu University
Department of Mechanical Engineering
Hydraulics and Mechatronics
1-1 Yanagido
Gifu, 501-11
Japan

Iowa State University
Department of Electrical Engineering and Computer Engineering
Ames, IA 60011

Johannes Kepler Universität Linz
Austria

Louisiana State University
Industrial and Manufacturing Systems Engineering Department
College of Engineering
3128 CEBA Building
Baton Rouge, LA

Katholieke Universiteit Leuven
Department of Mechanical Engineering Division of Production Engineering
Machine Design and Automation (PMA)
Celestihnenlaan 300B
B-3001 Leuven, Belgium

King's College London
Strand, London, WC2R 2LS
U.K.

Lancaster University
U.K.

Nagoya University
Department of Mechano-Informatics and Systems
Furo Cho, Chikusa-Ku
Nagoya, 464-01
Japan

NVFT (Niederlandse Vereiniging voor Fijnmechanische Techniek)
W te.Gussinklo
Postbus 359
5600 AJ Eindhoven
The Netherlands

Ohio State University
Department of Mechanical Engineering
Department of Electrical Engineering
Columbus, OH 43210

Penn State
Mechanical Engineering
Reber Mechanical Engineering Building
University Park, PA 46802

Purdue University
School of Mechanical Engineering
1288 Mechanical Engineering Building
West Layfayette, IN 47907-1288

Rensselaer Polytechnic Institute
Center for Manufacturing Productivity and Technology Transfer
Troy, NY 12180-3590

Stanford University
Design Division of Mechanical Engineering
Palo Alto, CA

Swiss Federal Institute of Technology
Department of Mechanical and Industrial Engineering
Switzerland

Tampere University of Technology
Edutech
P.O. Box 527
SF-33101 Tampere
Finland

Technical University in Darmstadt
Darmstadt
Germany

Telefunken Systemtechnik GMBH
Sedanstrasse 10
D-7900 Ulm (Donau)
Germany

Tohohashi University
Japan

Tohoku University
Department of Mechatronics and Precision Engineering
Aramaki-Aoba, Aobaku
Sendai, 980
Japan

Tokyo Institute of Technology
Department of Mechanical and Intelligent Systems Engineering
2-21-1 Ohokayama, Meguro-Ku
Tokyo, 152
Japan

Tokyo Metropolitan University
Robotics, Mechatronics, Single Board Computers
1-1 Minami Ohsawa, Hachioji-Shi
Tokyo, 192-03
Japan

TU Stuttgart
Institute for Time Measurement, Fine and Microtechnics
Breitscheidstr. 2b
D-7000 Stuttgart 1
Germany

TU-Vienna
Institute of Mechatronics
Gusshausstrasse 27-29
A-1040 Vienna
Austria

TU Wuppertal
Institute for Electromechanical Design
Fuhlrottstrasse 10
D-5600 Wuppertal 1
Germany

University of California at Berkeley
Mechanical Engineering Department
Berkeley, CA

University of Delaware
Applied Science and Engineering Laboratories
Alfred I. duPont Institute
P.O. Box 269
Wilmington, DE 19899

University of Dortmund
Dortmund
Germany

University of Dundee
Department of Applied Physics and Electronic and Manufacturing Engineering
Dundee DDI 4HN
Scotland, U.K.

University of Hull
U.K.

University of Kaiserslautern
Kaiserslautern
Germany

University of Kentucky
Center for Robotics and Manufacturing Systems
S. Limestone
Lexington, KY 40506

University of Leeds
Leeds, LS2 9JT
U.K.

University of South Carolina
Department of Mechanical Engineering
Columbia, SC 29208

University of Sydney
Department of Mechanical and Mechatronic Engineering
New South Wales
Australia

University of Technology, Loughborough
The Department of Mechanical Engineering
Leicestershire, LE11 3TU
U.K.

University of Tokyo
Department of Precision Machinery Engineering
Tokyo
Japan

University of Twente
Mechatronic Research Center Twente
Netherlands

University of Vesprem
Department of Information Technology and Automation
Vesprem
Hungary

University of Waikato
Physics Department
Hamilton
New Zealand

University of Washington
Department of Electrical Engineering
Seattle, WA 98195

Appendix

B

Vendor List

Introduction

This appendix provides a representative sample of the tools that are currently provided by many major MCAD/ECAD vendors today that can assist the mechatronic designer in product design. To be included in this appendix, a vendor has at least one product to assist the mechatronic designer. In many cases a vendor has many other products that typically focus solely on the MCAD or ECAD area.

This appendix is broken into several sections, which tends to follow the industry segmentation. Within the mechanical section products that cover electronic design problems have been covered. Likewise in the electronic section products that cover mechanical design problems are covered. To bridge these mechanical and electronic areas, products that facilitate information exchange and product data management have been included.

Mechanical

Product: AutoCAD®

Function. Autodesk provides a suite of products under the product name AutoCAD. These products used to focus primarily on the low-end mechanical drafting market. Recently, however, AutoCAD has added a suite of products to do surfacing (AutoCAD/AutoSurf) solid modeling as part of core AutoCAD, as well as solid modeling [Advanced Modeling Extension (AME)].

With release 12 Autodesk announced AutoCAD Data Extension (ADE). This software allows the user to reference geometry defined in multiple drawings and "assemble" needed elements together. This capability allows the user to build product assemblies. The development of product assemblies is a critical element in mechatronic product design.

On top of the above-mentioned AutoCAD capabilities are a variety of third-party vendors that assist the mechatronic designer to create a complete product design. Some of these vendors are highlighted individually (CADSI's DADS).

Interoperability. Autodesk was the first major CAD/CAM vendor to proliferate the concept of an open architecture. This allows end users and third-party vendors to provide a variety of levels of interoperability with core AutoCAD.

The first level of interoperability is by the exchange of .DXF and .DWG. These files allow the complete geometry definition, as well as all drawing annotations, to be transferred between AutoCAD applications, or between AutoCAD and other applications. Owing to the proliferation of AutoCAD .DXF and .DXG files are even transferred between AutoCAD-based applications and non-AutoCAD applications. For example, some ECAD allow the to develop a PCB outline in AutoCAD, and then upload this geometry to a PCB ECAD tool for PCB layout.

The definition of the .DXF and .DXG file formats can be obtained by writing directly to Autodesk.

The second level of interoperability is in the software architecture of AutoCAD itself. This architecture has allowed over 1500 software developers to create AutoCAD applications through the Autodesk Registered Developer Program^{SM}, serving a total customer base of over 1 million users.

AutoCAD developers do have standardization in the areas that Autodesk has developed as core applications. Therefore, because solid models are part of the core AutoCAD, a PCB that is laid out graphically with the base AutoCAD solid modeling functionality will be able to be rendered with Autodesk's AutoVision or 3D Studio's suite of applications. However, this same model will have no electrical design information.

Furthermore, if one electrical schematic vendor creates a schematic capture tool on top of AutoCAD there is no guarantee that this information can be sent to a PCB design automation tool running on top of AutoCAD. Autodesk itself assists in interoperability at the drawing, wireframe, and solids level of product definition. Interoperability at the product definition level is only achieved if the various industries cooperate to define common data formats.

Autodesk itself does not take an active role in promoting the transfer of mechatronic design information between its 1500 registered developers.

Hardware requirements. AutoCAD Release 12 supports:

- IBM 386-class machines with 8 Mbits RAM and 11 to 23 Mbits disk space for software.
- Quadra Series 700, 800, 900, and 950; Centris 650; Mac IIci, IIcx, IIvx, IIsi, IIfx, and IIx; SE/30; PowerBook 170 and 180, Duo 210 and 230; and LCII. All Macintosh machines must be equipped with a math coprocessor. Machines need 8 Mbits RAM, minimum, and 30 Mbits of disk space for complete installation of AME.
- UNIX workstations: DEC stations, HP-UX 9000/700 series, IBM RISC System/6000, IRIS Indigo, Sun-4, SPARC station, and Sun Solaris SPARC station. All workstations should be configured with a minimum of 16 to 32 Mbits of RAM, and 30 Mbits of disk space for a complete AME installation.

Vendor

Autodesk, Inc.
2320 Marinship Way
Sausalito, CA 94965
Tel: (415) 332-2344

Product: Bravo

Function. Bravo is the name given by Applicon Inc. for a family of MCAD/MCAE/MCAM products. In the year the product line was launched, 1983, it was named product of the year by *Fortune* magazine.

Within the Bravo product line are several modules that assist the mechatronic designer. The BravoMechanisms and BravoKinematics allow the user to build software prototypes of 3D mechanical systems. These prototypes can be analyzed for displacements, velocities, accelerations, and forces.

The BravoHarness module allows the user to model the wiring and wire harness interconnects within a product. Though Applicon does not sell schematic capture software the user can interface to existing schematic capture tools via a “from-to” list. The “from-to” list is then used to drive the routing of wires and harnesses. BravoHarness extends the mechanical design capabilities of BravoDesigner by allowing the user to define vectors to offset the centerline of a harness from mechanical design geometry. This offset distance can be based on the diameter of the wire or bundle.

Once the harness paths have been found, a fully automatic algorithm can be used to route the wires into the harness by choosing the shortest path. Once fully routed, the harness can be automatically or interactively unfolded to produce formboard drawings. The formboard drawings are used in the manufacture of the product.

Applicon has also established an interface to Cadence. This interface allows the mechanical aspects of PCB design to be developed in Applicon. The designer can specify initial PCB geometry and transfer it to Cadence. Once the board is fully placed and routed, the final board geometry can be transferred back into BravoDesign, where it can be subjected to a full range of MCAD-based analysis, such as physical interference checks, vibration, or heat dissipation.

Interoperability. Applicon interfaces the mechatronic aspects of its products through a custom software and file formats. For example, BravoCadence interfaces to Cadence EDA tools via a proprietary interface defined by Applicon and Cadence. The BravoHarness package is somewhat freer in that it can interface to any wiring diagram package through a generic "from-to" file.

The BravoIGES module allows Bravo users to export or import purely mechanical information to other MCAD systems.

Vendor

Applicon Inc.

4251 Plymouth Rd.

P.O. Box 986

Ann Arbor, MI 48106-0986

Tel: (313) 995-6000

Fax: (313) 995-6171

Product: CADDS5

Function. CADDS5 is an evolution of one of the most widely used MCAD packages in the world. Computervision has also had other product lines such as CADDS 2, AutoPlace/AutoRoute under CADDS 4X, and Theda which have always kept Computervision focused on both the mechanical and electronic design arenas.

Today's Computervision products allow mechanical and electrical engineers to collaborate in a number of areas.

Concurrent assembly mock-up (CAMU) allows multiple designers to concurrently work on a digital prototype of the product. Any changes made by one designer are automatically reflected in another designer's view of the same assembly. Therefore, if a designer changes the space allocated for a rack of PCBs, this change is automatically reflected in the assembly of the detailer of the PCB rack.

For kinematic analysis the SystemsLab product allows the user to insert revolute, cylindric, gear, rack and pinion, or prismatic joints, to name a few, into a product. SystemLab then allows the user to define forces, torques, or other motion generators to be applied to any of the components of the mechanism. Interfaces to ADAMS and DADS allow the user to develop simulations that take into account both the mechanical nature of the mechanism as well as the electronic control mechanisms required to make the product work.

Board outlines and components can be automatically transferred into a CADDS5 assembly through the CADDS gateway. This gateway also allows full connectivity information to be transferred bidirectionally between CADDS and PCB design capture products such as those sold by INCASES GmbH.

Two products assist in the mechatronic design of cables and wiring in a product. Electrical Design Entry allows the user to capture wires, cables, splices, shields, and shield taps. This information can be used to drive simulations or drive the design of a 3D harness. The 3D Harness Layout package takes the net, wire, and cable information developed in Electrical Design Entry and walks the user through the complete design of a harness. Users can model connectors, clips, cable wrapping, and other components critical to the design of a harness. 3D Harness Layout has tools to assist in the rapid layout of the harness centerlines, followed by completely automated tools to route wires into the harness. The complete harness can then be automatically unfolded onto a formboard in support of the manufacturing process.

Interoperability. The CADDS5 product line allows interoperation at several different levels. The Gateway product is tailored to allow schematic and PCB information to flow in and out of CADDS5. CADDS5 supports both IGES and STEP interfaces that allow users to share design information with other CAD vendors.

Computervision also provides an API product known as CV Dors. This product provides a development environment whereby third-party developers can use either a functional or object-based paradigm to interface to the functions of CADDS5.

Hardware requirements. Digital Alpha running AXP/OSF 1, Hewlett-Packard Series 700 running HP-UX, Silicon Graphics IRIX, and Sun SPARC running SunOS or Solaris.

Vendor

Computervision
100 Crosby Drive
Bedford, MA 01730
Tel: (617) 275-1800

Product: CATIA®

Function. CATIA is the general product name for one of the richest families of MCAD products on the market today. Even though CATIA has been predominantly an MCAD-focused product, there are several products in the CATIA family that focus on the common design problems faced by mechanical and electrical engineers.

From a top-down product structure point of view CATIA's Assembly Design and Assembly Modeling products allow the user to do system design. With system design a design can model components in the context of each other, as they would exist in the real product. For example, the outline of a PCB can be developed in the context of its mechanical enclosure. Likewise cables and wiring can be developed in the context of the rest of the product.

CATIA's assembly capability also allows joints to be modeled directly into the part at the time the assembly is designed. This means that downstream kinematic simulations can be fed information from work that went on in the very early stages of product definition and assembly. Good kinematic simulations have a direct tie into the ability of a company to do complete product modeling that includes control algorithms as well as the kinematic behavior of the product.

On a more electrical level, but still in the context of mechanical products CATIA offers a suite of products to design all the cabling and harness interconnects that are required to allow electronic modules within a product to communicate and be fed power. CATIA electrical Device and Support Modeling Product allows a design to model the mechanical aspects of connectors, terminal blocks, ground studs, etc. The electrical parts (though mechanical models) can be checked for system-imposed electrical consistency prior to filing the parts.

The CATIA Electrical Wire Bundle Installation product then allows the user to create a 3D model of Electrical Wire Bundles (sometimes referred to as wire harnesses). This product takes into account problems such as slack between two supports, automatic connector alignment between connector pairs, and automatic wire length calculation.

The CATIA Electrical Generative Formboard product allows users to automatically take a 3D bundle design developed with the electrical Wire Bundle Installation and create a 2D formboard layout. Into this layout wires can automatically be routed. The wire definitions can come through company-specific databases or applications through the Electrical Generative Formboard's open architecture. The products, Electrical Device and Support Modeling, Electrical Wire Bundle Installation, and Electrical Generative Formboard automate the otherwise time-consuming problem of transforming an electrical engineer's component interconnects as represented on a wiring diagram into the necessary formboards required for manufacturing.

Interoperability. CATIA products conform to PDES, STEP, and IGES to ensure maximum efficiency in design transfer to other systems. In addition electrical Generative Formboard provides an open architecture that allows customers to interface other wire list generation systems into the product.

Hardware requirements. CATIA operators on IBM's RS/6000 work stations with the AIX operating system and on IBM System/9000™, IBM 309x, and 43xx series mainframes running MVS/ESA™ or VM/ESA®.

Vendor

International Business Machines

1935 N. Buena Vista St.

Burbank, CA 91504-3341

Tel: (818) 559-3600

Product: Pro/ENGINEER®

Function. Pro/ENGINEER provides the core parametric modeling capabilities for Parametric Technology Corporation's (PTC) Mechatronic Design products. In addition to Pro/ENGINEER there are several application-specific products that address particular needs of the mechatronic designer.

Pro/ENGINEER itself allows the user to create parametric, feature-based solid models of a product. The parametric models are fully associative between all the design disciplines. Therefore, the keepouts on a PCB could automatically change in size as the overall PCB outline changes in size. Or a wire harness could be defined to be parallel to a series of surfaces and at a constant offset from these surfaces. If the user changes the geometry of the surfaces, the harness would automatically be moved to remain at the same offset. Likewise as more wires were routed into the harness the harness centerline would automatically be further offset from the surfaces to reflect the new harness diameter.

Of specific interest to the mechatronic designer are several products that cross the electromechanical border. The first product, which to some starts the design process, is Pro/DIAGRAM™. This tool allows the user to create electrical wiring diagrams. These wiring diagrams capture the specific wire interconnects between connectors and components. The diagrams support basic wiring diagram capabilities such as wire blanking, wire colors, and cross page connectors.

Pro/CABLING™ is the recipient of the wiring diagrams developed with Pro/DIAGRAM. This product makes full use of the Pro/ENGINEER associativity, as previously mentioned. This associativity allows the designer to ensure that the electrical requirements for connectivity between the wires and connectors is maintained by always keeping wire length information up-to-date, even as the underlying mechanical geometry of the product is changed. In addition Pro/CABLING allows the user to use a simple point and click paradigm to define cable paths. Pro/CABLING also highlights the appropriate "from" and "to" connectors to guide the user to properly define cable paths. The user can then easily construct the cable geometry between the from and to pair of connectors.

The final step in the Pro/DIAGRAM, Pro/CABLING sequence is Pro/HARNESS-MFG™. Pro/HARNESS-MFG allows the user to create manufacturing drawings using the cable and harness layouts created with Pro/CABLING. These drawings, in either stick figure or full-scale nail board drawings, allow the user to create all the documentation necessary to manufacture a cable or harness. Consistent with the core of this system the layouts created with Pro/HARNESS-MFG have associativity with the original 3D layouts created with Pro/CABLING. Diameter information which is derived from the "wire lists" is associative with the Pro/HARNESS-MFG version of the cable or harness. As the diameters of cables in the 3D assembly change, the same diameters in the 2D manufacturing drawing change automatically. Furthermore reports created with Pro/REPORT™ used to display a list of wires connected to a connector will be automatically updated as wires are added or subtracted to the connector.

Pro/ECAD™ is a generic tool that allows PCB design information that has been developed in an ECAD system to be imported or exported into Pro/ENGINEER. Pro/ECAD can maintain geometric information such as the PCB outline, edge connectors, mounting and alignment holes, 2D cutout areas for large components or housings, etch keep-out areas, and height restrictions. All this information can be downloaded to the ECAD system. Likewise component locations, 2D profiles, and height information can be automatically transferred into Pro/ECAD from the ECAD system. Pro/ECAD has been integrated with many of the major EDA packages supplied by Mentor, Cadence, Harris, Integraph, or Zuken/Redac.

Interoperability. There is a very tight coupling between Pro/DIAGRAM and Pro/CABLING. For example, the user is able to select a connector on a schematic and use the wires connected to this connector in the cabling operations within Pro/CABLING.

Over 70 of the major application vendors in the ECAD and MCAD arena have interfaced to Pro/ENGINEER through Pro/DEVELOP™, a software developer's tool kit. The extensive use of Pro/DEVELOP by these third-party suppliers has enabled PTC's packages to be very interoperable with a wide variety of software tools.

Hardware requirements. The Pro/Engineer family of products runs on all major UNIX, VMS, and Windows NT-based workstations.

Vendor

Parametric Technology
128 Technology Drive
Waltham, MA 02154
Tel: (617) 398-5000
Fax: (617) 398-6000

Information Exchange

Product: ST-203, ST-Express, ST-Developer, ST-Visualizer™

Function. STEP is an emerging standard for CAD data transfer between various CAD systems. STEP allows for the transfer of geometry as well as providing application protocols for the transfer of electrical, mechanical, and a variety of other applications. STEP is unlike IGES which only transfers the geometry of a product. All application-specific data are lost with IGES. To support the transfer of data between CAD systems, STEP Tools Inc. has developed ST-203,

ST-Express, ST-Developer, and ST-Visualizer. In addition there exist interfaces developed with STEP Tool Inc.'s software to IGES, DXF, CADDS, ACIS, CATIA, ObjectStore, HP OpenODB, Pro/ENGINEER, and other applications.

The STEP standards committee has developed a specification for the STEP information model called EXPRESS. STEP Tools Inc. has built a set of tools to help work with this information model. The STEP standards, as well as interfaces to DXF, IGES, and other CAD formats, have all been described using data schemas using EXPRESS. In addition CAD Framework Initiative (CFI) and Petrotechnical Open Software Corporation (POSC) have also created EXPRESS information models. This enables the data created through the standards of these two initiatives to be converted to STEP and vice versa with tools provided by STEP Tools Inc. In particular a graphic representation of the information model, called EXPRESS-G, was created by STEP Tools Inc. to allow one to see a visual representation of the information model.

ST-203 manages databases of AP 203 data. ST-203 will convert IGES data and data from a variety of CAD systems into fully conformant AP 203 data.

ST-Express is a tool that allows the user to create an information model for specific CAD data using the EXPRESS language. This tool will output files in the EXPRESS language. These language files are schemas for the information model and used as input to the Express interpreter. The Express interpreter ensures that a data set which describes a part matches the schema definition.

ST-Visualizer offers the visualization routines of ST-203 in a library form that allows an application to visualize the geometry of models containing Part 42 of STEP. The application developer then embeds these routines into the application to get the graphics capabilities of ST-203.

ST-Developer allows an end user to map data sets between different schemas that have been defined with ST-Express. Thus a specific CAD vendor could create an EXPRESS information model that maps the database format into the EXPRESS information model for STEP or other CAD data formats. ST-Developer comes with libraries that meet the specifications of the STEP Data Access Interface (SDAI). The libraries are compatible with ANSI C, K&R C, and a wide range of C++ compilers.

Interoperability. The products made by STEP Tools Inc. are interoperable from both a hardware and a software point of view. In the hardware area the tools run on almost all popular workstation and PC platforms. In the software area STEP Tool's products are focused on making data interoperable between a variety of systems. The interoperability of data is STEP Tool's primary focus.

Hardware requirements. ST-Visualizer is written as an SGI Open Inventor application. It is supported on IRIX 5.2 and requires 5 to 7 Mbits of disk space.

ST-Developer works on SunOS 4.1.x or Solaris 2.3, HP9000 series 700 running HP-UX, IBM RS/6000 running AIX 3.2, DECstation running Ultirs, and Silicon Graphics running IRIX 4.05 and 5.0. This UNIX workstation requires a minimum of 16 Mbits of memory and 60 Mbits of disk space. ST-Developer also runs on the Windows NT operating system.

ST-Express runs on MS Windows with a 386 processor or compatible with 10 Mbits disk space and 8 Mbits memory running MS Windows V3.1.

Vendor

Step Tools, Inc.

Rensselaer Technology Park

Troy, NY 12180

Tel: (518) 276-2848

Fax: (518) 276-8471

Product: Brockware

Function. Brock Rooney and Associates markets a set of products under the family name "Brockware" which allows users of various CAD/CAM systems to interchange data or send data to a stereo lithography system.

At the heart of the conversion work is an IGES engine which allows data from various MCAD vendors to be read and then converted into a MCAD vendors native part format, or to a vendor, such as 3D Systems, native stereo lithography input format.

Because this system is only translating data that are based on part geometry and rely heavily on IGES, these products have minimal value to a mechatronic engineer. (They may of course be *very* valuable to a pure mechanical engineer.)

Hardware requirements. DOS-X, Sun, and SGI only.

Vendor

Brock Rooney & Associates, Inc.

268 George St.

Birmingham, MI 48009
Tel: (810) 645-0236
Fax: (810) 645-9020

Product Data Management

Product: Parts Management eXpert (CADIS-PMX)

Function. CADIS produces a family of products which allows a mechanical or electrical engineer to tap into the vast supply of existing component designs that have already been developed within the company. By reusing existing parts, a company can avoid significant costs associated with the release of new parts for a new design. The Part Life Cycle has been estimated to range from a low of $5000 to as high as $60,000 per part. These costs do not take into account the cost to manufacture the part, only the overhead required to manage that part through engineering, MRP, purchasing, receiving, quality inspection, etc.

For the mechatronics designer the ability to readily draw on parts from other product designs can free up a lot of the engineering analysis that would go into creating the parts from scratch. It also allows the mechatronics designer to quickly browse through the BOMs associated with many other product designs. The ability to browse through other designs is a critical tool that empowers engineers focused on a specific problem to bring experiences from many different product design cycles to the current problem.

The CADIS-PMX™ is used to store and provide fast access to a company's part information. Built into this package is a Universal Classification Schema that captures mechanical and electrical components.

The CADIS-PMX-Legacy™ is a service used to initially process and classify legacy parts data from MRP and other systems into the CADIS-PMX classification schema. By using the PMX system to initially search for a legacy part for reuse, as well as specify new parts if a suitable component is not found, the database is always current, and newly released parts are always fully described.

Some CADIS-PMX customers have extended the attribute information stored into the classification schema to include design and service parameters to aid engineers in the proper selection of a component. For example, if a particular component was designed for 1000 life cycles, this information would be recorded in the schema so that the component would not be selected for a product that required

1 million life cycles. Similarly failure rate in components can be fed into the schema so that poor product designs can be avoided or improved on before they are incorporated into another product.

Interoperability. The CADIS-PMX suite of products is built on top of an object-oriented knowledge base and classification schema which is built from C++ objects. Interfacing the knowledge base to other systems such as MRP, CAD, or PDM is done via the CADIS-API or via consultancy services provided by CADIS.

The result of using CADIS-PMX is both a list of candidate part numbers and the capability to review the part drawings associated with these part numbers. PMX can launch CAD software application or viewer software. PMX hands the part number to the appropriate software through a "user action" inside PMX. Drawings of selected part(s) are pulled up within the PMX application.

Hardware requirements. Server: Unix SUNOS, Solaris, HP 9000, IBM RS 6000. Clients: PC486 or Unix/Motif.

Vendor

CADIS, Inc.
1909 26th Street
Boulder, CO 80302
Tel: (303) 440-4363
Fax: (303) 440-5309

Product: EDM

Function. The EDM family of products provide end users with controlled access to computer-based data files such as part drawings, business plans, or wiring diagrams. By allowing immediate access to full product information, barriers between mechanical and electrical engineering departments can start to be overcome.

EDMVault™ is the heart of the EDM family of products. EDMVault manages and catalogs information such as CAE/CAD/CAM drawings, models, raster images, or technical publications. EDMVault itself allows all end users, whether on PCs or workstations, to gain access to any document stored within the vault, provided that they have the authorization to do so. EDMVault also controls access to information to ensure that only one person at a time is making a change to the information in a vault. These capabilities are critical in a mechatronic design approach where, for example, both mechanical and electrical engineers can be editing bills of materials or checking the location of a limit switch in a mechanism.

EDMNavigator™ delivers the benefits of engineering data management to the end user. Users or software programs can locate, retrieve, and manipulate data files stored anywhere in EDMVault. The graphical user interface allows users to view products simply as a list of part numbers or view a product configuration displayed as a hierarchical tree.

Distributed Vaulting™ extends the use of the EDMVault by allowing multiple vaults to be linked electronically no matter where the information is located. This feature facilitates a central design center distributing design information to manufacturing sites located in different parts of the world.

EDMProjects provides a tool for capturing work and describing the criteria for moving between tasks. In this way, for example, a project leader for a product could make sure that all changes to a product's mechanisms are routed through the electrical engineering department to make sure that the motors and control algorithms can still make the product work successfully. EDMProject supports the novel concept of "voting," whereby everyone that has the right to approve a design can vote pass/fail. The design then moves to the next step if there are a sufficient number of passes.

Interoperability. The EDM products work with Oracle running on Sun, DEC, HP, RS6000, and Windows/NT.

Platform and network configurations. DEC Alpha AXP, DEC VAX, HP 9000, IBM PC compatibles (client), IBM RS6000, Silicon Graphics (client), Sun SPARC, Windows/NT, TCP/IP (IEEE 802.3).

Vendor

Computervision Corporation
100 Crosby Drive
Bedford, MA 01730-1480
Tel: (617) 275-1800

Product: Matrix

Function. The matrix system takes a very novel approach to the PDM problems of a company. Matrix is built as a very easy to use and scalable system. These two features make it extremely attractive for small to medium-sized engineering groups to coordinate the activities of their mechanical and electrical engineering departments.

Ease of use is apparent at every level of operation. Engineer end users can be acting in several roles. For example, if they are part of the release process for a particular product, designs to review will simply show up in the user's mail tool. The mail tool is used to handle the general routing of all product information from user to user. Similarly an engineer who is responsible for initiating a change to a design can make this change. After the change is made, the design will automatically be routed to the necessary people for checking or to support downstream processes.

A user who wants to select a design to review information about it or make a change can simply browse through the designs by filtering on an attribute of the design or by visually searching through stored graphical samples of the actual drawings. A combination of filtering and looking at graphical samples greatly facilitates design retrieval and reuse.

Further support for the implementation of PDM with Matrix is provided by a set of tools that manage the overall PDM process itself. However, unlike other PDM products, Matrix allows the user to directly model the objects, organization, and processes in the organization as they exist in the real world. Organizations can be described as groups of people. Thus there could be a mechanical and electrical engineering group. Each of these groups would have several people assigned.

Within this organization structure processes can be defined. For example, some of the people within the mechanical engineering group could be assigned to review the designs from the electrical engineering department.

The data objects have associated with them the tools that can be used to open and edit the objects. Therefore, a design that originates in the mechanical engineering department might appear in the mailbox of one of the engineers in the electrical engineering department. By selecting this mail message, the electrical engineer would cause the design to be automatically opened for viewing by the associated application.

Scalability is inherent in the peer-to-peer distributed architecture used in Matrix. The Matrix System does not use a centralized database. All databases can be federated anywhere in a networked systems environment. When a new user and system are added, the user's profile is established along with the information, applications, and processes required.

Interoperability. Matrix System is designed to allow multiple applications to be integrated. By associating applications with each object, Matrix allows users to receive objects and quickly access the information in the object without worrying about the tools used in the process.

Furthermore if a translation is required to output an IGES file from an ECAD PCB application so that the outline of the board can be viewed by the mechanical engineering department, this filtering can automatically be incorporated such that the IGES files are generated every time the PCB design is saved.

Hardware requirements. Matrix is available on the following leading UNIX-based workstations: Sun Microsystems, Hewlett-Packard, IBM, Silicon Graphics, and Digital Equipment Corporation. These platforms will quickly be extended to include Microsoft Windows and Microsoft Windows NT. The Matrix System is implemented as a peer-to-peer architecture. Therefore, as more end users are added there is no need to continually upgrade the resources of the central server.

Vendor

Adra Systems
Two Executive Drive
Chelmsford, MA 01824
Tel: (508) 937-3700
Fax: (508) 453-2462

Product: Sherpa/PIMS

Function. Sherpa is the leading independent Product Data Management market (PDM) vendor with over 50,000 PIMS "seats" currently installed. PIMS offers an array of document management tools that make it an absolute must for any company that wants to use a mechatronic design strategy. PIMS supports several major functional areas that are critical to the concurrent engineering required by a mechatronics design approach, Engineering Change Management, Engineering Work in Progress, and Documentation Vault.

Engineering Work in Progress (EWIP) and Engineering Change Management are two of the most important functional areas for the mechatronic designer. The EWIP allows the organization to determine what sign-off permissions are required in order for a particular product component to be approved. This capability, for example, could be used to make sure that the electrical engineer has sign-off approval on selection of cooling systems for a particular system. Likewise a mechanical engineer could be required to sign off on the design of a PCB to make sure mounting bosses are incorporated at the same location as the mounting holes on the PCB. Similar to the EWIP functions, the Engineering Change Management functions allow the corporation to tailor the full Engineering Change process. Not only can the process be enforced, but it also can be tracked. PIMS will know if sign-off on a particular change is being held up in a particular department because it tracks the change process.

PIMS is not just about controlling the EWIP or Engineering Change process. It also allows each user to access all the information pertinent to the product design and its life cycle through the Object Vault. Any object, whether they be the product's business plan, CAD design files, NC programs, or manufacturing process sheets, can be managed within the Object Vault. A single controlled archive for this information means that there is far less chance for decisions to be made on an incorrect version of the data. Furthermore the delay typically associated with getting access to the information is reduced to the few seconds it takes for the data to be downloaded and the correct application started to view the information.

Sherpa's product offering also allows the user to define product structure, configuration management, report generation, as well as customization tools and integration to MRP systems.

Interoperability. The PIMS product is highly interoperable, from both a hardware and a software point of view. After a document is fetched from the vault, PIMS can automatically launch the appropriate application and load the document. PIMS also allows the user to archive a wide range of data about a product. The user is not restricted to archiving only ECAD/MCAD data. Spreadsheets, word processing documents, or straight text files can also be archived.

The user interface can be run in OPEN LOOK or Motif, X-Windows, or windows mode.

Hardware requirements. VAX/VMS, all major UNIX workstations, IBM compatibles running Windows or Window-NT, and Macintosh. PIMS typically is run in a distributed hardware environment. Therefore, PIMS supports TCP/IP, DECNet, Ethernet, and Novel network models.

Vendor

Sherpa Corporation

611 River Oaks Parkway

San Jose, CA 95134

Tel: (800) PDM-XPRT

Fax: (408) 943-6622

Analysis

Forms of mechatronic analysis typically go above and beyond, for example, the application of finite element meshing to determine heat transfer or stress on a product. Analysis can vary from simulation of the mechatronic product itself, to visualization of the man-machine interface, to detecting potential EMI/EMC problems.

Product: ACIS®

Function. ACIS solves two big problems with one solution. First, the ACIS Geometric Modeler provides a rich set of wire, surface, and solids based tools all built with C++. These tools allow users to create solids and then use boolean operators to combine them into more complex objects. Many companies and universities, such as Autodesk, Ford Motor Company, and Carnegie-Mellon University, have used this modeler to develop commercial, in-house, or educational software applications. One of the major advantages of this modeler is that it allows the application developer or university to focus on their specific value added. Therefore, a company like Autodesk can focus on the integration of its application suite instead of geometric modeling, which is becoming a commodity technology.

Likewise universities that want to teach mechatronic concepts can build on top of an existing, robust modeling system without having to devote extensive class time to the geometric modeling problem itself. This allows students to focus on what the geometric model is actually trying to represent. A student of mechatronics can focus on the more global product level rather than the geometric modeling of individual piece parts.

ACIS is built on top of C++. This language has several major benefits. Unlike Smalltalk or Lisp C++ has widely become the industry standard for Object Oriented software development. This enables software written in C++ to be readily ported across multiple platforms. The Object Oriented paradigm itself also allows applications built on top of ACIS to be able to extend the richness of the geometric model without having to reimplement any of the underlying model.

For example, an application could model a limit switch and the sensing envelope of the switch. The application could then manipulate the part until another part of the model tripped the limit switch by entering the sensor envelope. All the Boolean operators that detected whether any other part of the product had entered the sensor envelope would be able to work uniformly because they were all built from the ACIS geometry modeler where all solid models understand how to do boolean intersections.

The second problem the ACIS geometric modeler solves is that it enables many applications to share information. There is an increasing trend for third-party developers or major MCAD/MCAM develop-

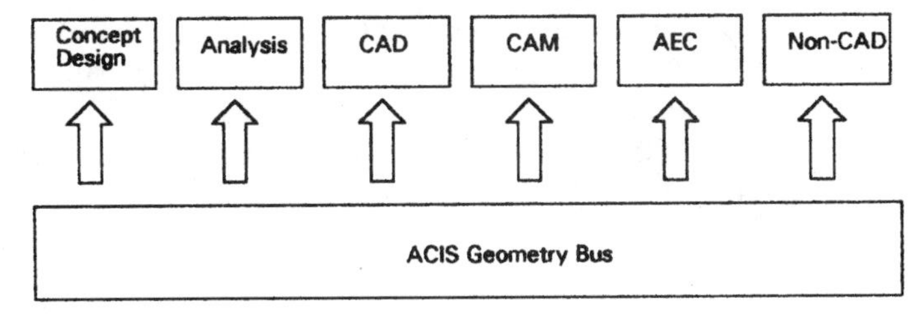

Figure B.1 Common geometry bus.

ment houses to interface or incorporate ACIS directly into their products. Whereas users used to have to use IGES or STEP to transmit geometry from one application to another, all the various applications can now sit on top of one common geometry bus. As depicted in Fig. B.1 this geometry bus allows multiple applications to readily communicate with each other.

The Spatial Technology approach to application development presents a major paradigm shift for the MCAD/MCAE industry. It moves value-added applications provided by vendors onto a common geometric platform. This is equivalent to the convergence of many applications to the DOS operating system in the seventies and eighties.

The trend has started for software vendors to build applications on top of the C++ geometry bus. This opens the door for other companies to provide an application layer on top of ACIS which contains all the necessary attributes and intelligence for a particular industry. Imagine, for example, being above the geometry bus to associate the electromagnetic interference (EMI) associated with each piece of geometry in an application. If this could be represented as a set of C++ methods on top of the geometric model, then all applications that wanted to do EMI analysis on a product would be able to communicate with each other.

Interoperability. The ACIS geometric modeler allows users to put attributes in the geometry model at any level. Therefore, a solid could have an attribute indicating it models a solenoid or a particular face could have an attribute indicating it is the hard limit for a link in a robot arm.

Spatial technology is currently working on standardizing the attributes and features associated with the ACIS geometry model. With these developments ACIS will stand well above other pure data transfer protocols such as IGES, STEP, or PDES. ACIS will be able to transfer geometry, features, and attributes as data along with the behavior of the geometry, features, and attributes. The transfer of behaviors at the feature and attribute level truly distinguishes this product.

Hardware requirements. True to Spatial Technology's desire to achieve wide acceptance and interoperability, their products run on HP 9000, SparcStation/Sun4, SGI Personal Iris/Indigo, DecStation 3000 and 5000 series, VAXStation 3100, and IBM RS/6000 running Windows, Windows NT, UNIX, and VMS.

Vendor

Spatial Technology Inc.
2425 55th Street, Bldg. A
Boulder, CO 80301-5704
Tel: (303) 449-0649
Fax: (303) 943-6622

Product: ADAMS®

Function. Mechanical Dynamics Inc. (MDI) is the market leader in the mechanical simulation market. MDI's product, ADAMS, is sold standalone by MDI or can be bought as an interfaced solution from most of the major MCAD vendors. MDI calls their modeling and simulation capability Virtual Prototyping because it allows a designer to create a full working prototype of the product without ever having to fabricate any piece part in the product.

ADAMS/View, and ADAMS/Solver are the two modules that allow the user to develop a mechanical simulation. ADAMS/View allows the user to either import CAD geometry from another system or model it directly. ADAMS/View also allows the user to place over 50 joint types, forces, and motion generators. ADAMS/Solver is used to run the kinematic simulation of the mechanism. Sensitivity data can be developed by using a "design-of-experiments" capability.

Of great importance to the mechatronic designer is to be able to test the control algorithms that are going to be implemented on an embedded microprocessor in the context of the virtual prototype. The ADAMS/linear tool allows the control and feedback systems to be incorporated directly into the overall simulation. ADAMS/linear exports linearized representations of nonlinear multibody assemblies in both eigendata and state matrix form. These data are exported in a form suitable for input to $MATRIX_x$® and MATLAB™. After the controls design is complete, the designer can incorporate it into a full closed-loop ADAMS model. ADAMS then simulates the complete control system.

Interoperability. MDI has been a company for over 17 years. Therefore, it has had the opportunity to tightly couple its simulation capabilities into most of the MCAD offerings of Application, Aries, Computervision, EDS/Unigraphics, IBM, Integraph, Matra, Parametric Technologies, and SDRC.

Hardware requirements. SGI, HP, Sun, IBM, and DEC Unix workstations, Cray, Convex supercomputers, Intel 386/486, and Pentium based PCs.

Vendor

Mechanical Dynamics, Inc.

2301 Commonwealth Boulevard

Ann Arbor, MI 48105

Tel: (313) 994-3800

Fax: (313) 994-6418

Product: DFA

Function. BDI offers a suite of products to analyze the manufacturability and serviceability of products under design. These products are:

- DFA
- PCB DFA
- Die Casting
- Machining
- DFS
- Sheet Metalworking
- Powder Metal
- Injection Molding

On the surface it might appear that these products are focused on the vertical integration between design and manufacturing. However, that doesn't paint a complete picture. First, the DFM tools are used at the design stage of the product life cycle. Second, trade-offs can be made between the mechanical and electrical aspects of a product which in turn can make the manufacturing of the product less expensive (see Fig. B.2).

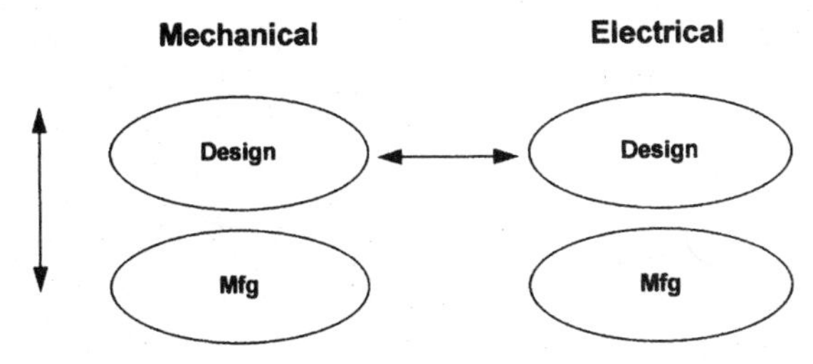

Figure B.2 Mechanical and electrical trade-offs.

For example, IBM used the Design for Assembly product to analyze the design of the Proprinter. One portion of the study found that three of the parts in the Proprinter could be eliminated through product redesign. These three parts turned out to be electrical connectors. The integration of the connectors into the assembly would save 12 seconds per printer or increase production by over 2000 units per year.

A similar analysis was performed by Motorola for their Saber VA vehicle adapter. By using DFA the Motorola team was able to cut assembly time from 2742 down to 354 seconds per unit. Most importantly a lot of this assembly time reduction was a result of changing the way electronics were packaged into the product. For example, instead of having two circuit boards at right angles to each other with the resultant interconnection problems solved by a mass of jumper cables, the new assembly relied on a flat circuit board with surface-mounted components.

The Printed Circuit Board Design for Assembly product has been jointly developed by Boothroyd Dewhurst and the Concurrent Engineering Products Group of Texas Instruments, Inc. This product provides a library of industry-proven components developed by BDI/TI for the PCB DFA software. This library can be matched to in-house components such that designers can take advantage of the data collected by BDI/TI over the past 10 years.

Interoperability. BDI's products run standalone on IBM-compatible PCs. The BDI DFA product is also directly integrated into Parametric Technology's ProENGINEER product on a variety of workstations.

Hardware requirements. IBM compatible PC's 386Processor 4-Mbit RAM 4-Mbit Hard Disk Space VGA monidor, DOS 3.3 Windows 3.1, HP 9000-700 series running UP-UX, SunSParc running Solaris 2.3.

Vendor

Boothroyd Dewhurst Inc.

138 Main St.

Wakefield, RI 02879

Tel: (401) 783-5840

Fax: (401) 783-6872

Product: COSMOS

Function. COMSMOS/EM features magnetostatic (2D and 3D), electrostatic (2D and 3D), current flow (2D and 3D), axisymmetric frequency domain (AC) (2D and 3D), transient eddy current, and nonlinear transient analysis. These tools can help mechatronics designers with design applications in the areas of transmission lines, magnetic field distribution in magnetic disk drives, electric motor design, or heat generation from current flows.

Interoperability. COSMOS interfaces through most standard MCAD packages through IGES or DXF interfaces. In addition direct links have been made to Pro/ENGINEER, and CADDS5.

Hardware requirements. Sun SPARCstatin, Sunr, SPARCserver, Hewlett-Packard 9000/700 series, Silicon Graphics Personal IRRIS, Indigo, Digital DECstation, DEC ALPHA 3000 series, IBM RS/6000. 32-Mbit memory required, 64 Mbits recommended. 150 Mbits disk space with an additional 50 Mbits for program storage. 386/486/Pentium-based IBM compatibles. 8-Mbit memory, 16 Mbits is strongly recommended. 50 Mbit-disk space, 200 Mbit disk space recommended. 80387 or equivalent math coprocessor required. Apple Computers: 18-Mbit memory, 24 Mbits strongly recommended. 40 Mbit disk, 160 Mbits recommended. Math coprocessor required.

Vendor

Structural Research & Analysis Corp.
2951 28th Street, Suite 1000
Santa Monica, CA 90405
Tel: (310) 452-2158
Fax: (310) 399-6421

Product: DADS®, DADS/Plant™

Function. DADS is one of the most widely used mechanical simulation tools on the market. DADS allows the designer to verify digital prototypes of a product by allowing the designer to study the motions of the product. DADS has been applied to tasks such as analyzing the simple latch motion of a door handle, or to complex simulations involving a flexible helicopter blade. The user can view the simulation as a dynamically moving shaded image, or review graphics for forces and accelerations.

DADS/Plant combines the simulation capabilities of DADS/Plant with controls modeling software such as MATRIX_x®, MATLAB™, and EASY5x®.* DADS/Plant eliminates the time-consuming, error-prone

*EASY5x is a registered trademark of Boeing Computer Services, MATLAB is a registered trademark of The MathWorks, Inc., and MATRIX_x is a registered trademark of Integrated Systems, Inc.

process of deriving and manipulating equations of motion for the model of a controls simulation program. The controls simulation program calls DADS/Plant at each integration time step and updates the mathematic model to maintain error control.

Interoperability. CADSI® analysis software is integrated with the following design and analysis programs: AutoCAD, CATIA, Pro/ENGINEER, ANSYS, Aries, COSMOS/M, SDRC I-DEAS, MSC/NASTRAN, and PDA/PATRAN. DADS supports the industry standard IGES interface to allow CAD models to be imported into the simulation environment.

Hardware requirements. UNIX workstations: DEC, HP, IBM, SGI, SUN, with appropriate graphics adapters.

Vendor

CADSI
2651 Crosspark Rd.
Coralville, IA 52241
Tel: (319) 626-6700
Fax: (319) 626-3488

Product: MAGNETO, AMPERES, OERSTED, FARADAY, ELECTRO, and COULOMB

Function. Integrated Engineering Software (IES) provides a suite of software tools that can be used for electromagnetic design and analysis. These tools are especially interesting to the mechatronic designer because they allow the designer to model magnetic fields in either two- or three-dimensional mechanical products. Each of the software tools uses the boundary element method (BEM) to develop smooth accurate results to electromagnetic problems. The BEM is superior to the finite element method (FEM) because the user does not have to create a mesh to cover the air gaps or regions surrounding the geometry to model. The FEM also uses differentiation. Differentiation can lead to localized discontinuities in the model. The BEM eliminates both of these problems.

IES has created a very easy to use suite of software tools. In one case an undergraduate student learned to use the program in one hour. One week later she was doing sophisticated analysis for a project on impedance imaging.

MAGNETO (2D and rotationally symmetric) and AMPERES (3D) are used to solve magnetostatic problems. These problems are commonly found in permanent magnet assemblies, recording heads, electric motors (at rest), or circuit breakers, to name a few. These two packages can calculate magnetic fields, potentials, forces, torques, and mutual and self-inductances.

OERSTED (2D and rotationally symmetric) and FARADAY (3D) are used to solve low-frequency time-harmonic field analysis problems. These problems are found in electric motors, bus bars, charging fixtures, induction heating/motors, coils, and transformers. These packages can calculate induced currents, magnetic and electric fields, skin and proximity effects, forces and torques, as well as resistance and inductance.

ELECTRO (2D and rotationally symmetric) and COULOMB (3D) can calculate voltage and electrical field components, electric field distributions, self- and mutual capacitances, inductances, impedance and propagation constants.

Interoperability. Data can be imported from a CAD system via an IGES translator. Data developed within any of the software packages can be shared with any of the other software packages in the IES software suite.

Hardware requirements. IBM, Sun SPARCstation, DEC Alpha, SGI Personal IRIS, and HP 9000/700 series workstations with a minimum of 16 Mbits RAM and 100 Mbits disk space for 2D applications, 400 Mbits disk space for 3D applications. Available on all IBM compatibles running DOS, Microsoft Windows v3.1, v3.11, NT v3.2, and NT v3.5 platforms. Recommend 16 to 32 Mbits of RAM.

Vendor

Integrated Engineering Software

46-1313 Border Place

Winnipeg, Manitoba, Canada

R3H 0X4

Tel: (204) 632-5636

Fax: (204) 633-7780

Product: MECHANICA®

Function. Rasna® Corporation offers the MECHANICA family of products to perform Mechanical Design Synthesis™. Design synthesis allows the designer to optimize a product's design by making tradeoffs between a large number of design criteria.

The MECHANICA product line is divided into two main areas. The motion area focuses on tools that are of direct benefit to the mechatronics designer. The structure side focuses more on the traditional heat, vibration, and structural analysis that one would associate with an FEA-based suite of tools.

The MECHANICA Motion™ module allows an engineer to create a mechanism model by importing CAD data from other systems or using library components such as joints or ground points. Once the mechanism has been assembled it can be simulated through advanced solution methods, such as Order N solution or modified Kane's method. Design parameters can be automatically varied to produce a sensitivity study of how the design parameters affect the resulting mechanism behavior.

Of special interest to the mechatronics designer is the MECHANICA Equations™ module. This module allows mechanisms developed with MECHANICA Motion to be interfaced to simulation programs. This interface allows the control algorithm of a mechanism to be fully analyzed in the context of the exact control algorithm that will be used to control the product.

The designer has several ways to model devices such as limit switches into the control model. MECHANICA supports a general facility called "measures." With measures the designer can detect a min/max or average position for a particular device. Therefore, the designer can detect the maximum position of a limit switch, for example. The designer can then develop a set of equations and logic statements that make use of the device being measured. Another scenario would be to export the kinematic motion equations into another simulator. In this scenario a user could model several discrete devices and then assemble the equations that model these devices into a product such as MATLAB, developed by The Math Works, to perform a simulation of a complete work cell along with all the control mechanisms.

Some mechatronics designers may want to do some of the more traditional thermal and vibrational analysis. For example, Textronix has used MECHANICA Thermal™ to analyze the heat-dissipation problems associated with mounting integrated chips onto a printed circuit board. The ease of use of MECHANICA, coupled with its ability to do sensitivity analysis, has brought thermal analysis back onto the desktops of engineers that at one time tried more complex finite element tools.

Interoperability. The MECHANICA family of products interface to the major CAD/CAM systems through neutral data files such as AutoCAD DXF Release 12, IGES Version 5.1, and IGES Solids Version 5.1. Rasna also supports custom interfaces to Pro/ENGINEER Release 12 and 13,

CADDS V Release 4 and 5, CATIA Release 3.2.5 and 4, and Unigraphics II Release 10.3. In addition MECHANICA Equations can interface to the following simulation packages: ACSL, Matrix X, ProMatlab, Easy 5, and Simulink.

Hardware requirements. MECHANICA runs on the UNIX workstations from Digital Equipment Corporation, Hewlett-Packard Company, IBM Corporation, Silicon Graphics, Inc., and Sun Microsystems, and on the leading UNIX-based workstations in Japan. MECHANICA is also available for Windows/NT-based personal computers and for Cray high-performance computers.

Vendor

Rasna Corporation
2590 North First St., Suite 200
San Jose, CA 95131
Tel: (800) 937-4432
Fax: (408) 922-7256

Product: MSC/EMAS

Function. The EMAS product is a finite element modeler. Until recently the product was limited to modeling either mechanical or electromagnetic problems. With Version 3 of MSC/EMAS a user can now model both electromagnetic and structural finite elements. This allows the mechatronic engineer to start to analyze some of the boundary problems between mechanics and electromagnetics. Specifically SOL 311 can compute nonlinear transient motion, forces, electromagnetic fields, and eddy current losses for devices that are both 2D and 3D. Examples of some of the types of problems that can now be tackled are described below.

For example, Dr. John Brauer presented a paper at the Compumag conference in November 1993. In this paper he describes work based on MSC/EMAS for solutions to the TEAM problem 12, as well as an axisymmetric solenoid actuator. The TEAM problem 12 consists of a cantilevered copper beam that is exposed to steady and transient magnetic fields. In the solenoid actuator problem the goal was to compute plunger displacements versus time based on the application of transient currents applied to the coil. In both cases MSC/EMAS was able to predict the behavior of the real physical model with less than 10 percent overall error.

The analysis of the solenoid was also able to predict the effects of eddy current on the motion of the solenoid itself. The analysis's predictions matched the reality of the device in that there was a 50-millisecond delay before the solenoid's plunger started to move owing to the effect of eddy currents.

MSC/EMAS has also proved capable of modeling the EMC/EMI effects found in some typical car configurations. In one example MSC/EMAS was used to analyze the EMI effects of a one- versus two-wire harness. The software was able to accurately predict the resulting fields from both of these scenarios. In another example MSC/EMAS was used to predict the radiated fields from a variety of different PCBs.

In the past designers were only able to consider a stationary mechanism with time-varying magnetic fields. These magnetic fields were typically changed by changes in a source coil current. Recently the MSC/EMAS software has been shown to be able to analyze eddy currents caused by motion of the conducting material with respect to the field.

The MSC/EMAS product has also been used to analyze multiturn windings with attached electric circuits. This allows the designer to determine the behavior of devices such as transformers or solenoids as they are subject to various circuits.

Interoperability. MSC/EMAS also communicates with standards-based CAD programs that support transfer protocols such as ACIS, IGES, DXF, and more.

Hardware requirements. Convex C2/C3 running ConvexOS 10.1, Cray Y-MP and C 90 running UNICOS 7.0, DEC Alpha running OSF/1 1.3 and OpenVMS 1.5, Digital VAX, HP 9000/700 and 800 running HP-UX 9.01, IBM RS/6000 running AIX 3.2.4, SGI running IRIX 5.0.1, SUN SPARC running Solaris 2.2 or SunOS 4.1.3. Most platforms require 32 Mbits of memory.

Vendor

The MacNeal-Schwendler Corporation

Engineering/Electromagnetic Applications

4200 West Brown Deer Road, Suite 300

Milwaukee, WI 53223-2465

Tel: (414) 357-8723

Fax: (414) 357-0347

Product: PCB/MCM SIGNAL INTEGRITY, VLSI SIGNAL INTEGRITY, PARASITIC PARAMETERS, PCB THERMAL, PCB SolderSim, PCB FATIGUE, PCB VIBRATION PLUS

Function. Pacific Numerix "Places Space Age Technology in the Hands of the Practical Engineer." For the most part these are electronic engineers capturing schematics and creating PCB or MCM layouts. Since 1987, Pacific Numerix has developed a suite of product that tightly couples the electronic designs to their physical implementation and performs electrical and mechanical design validations utilizing a single database obtained from various CAD/CAE systems.

The PCB/MCM and VLSI SIGNAL INTEGRITY tools allow engineers or designers to validate the signal integrity of an electronics design at any level in electronics packaging including system level. There are predesign, preroute (postlayout), and postroute modules for performing design validation throughout the design cycle. Artwork for traces, vias, and power/ground planes are read in from ECAD systems. Parasitic models of this artwork are created automatically. The frequency-dependent R,L,C,G parasitics are then extracted. SPICE models are automatically created utilizing the extracted artwork. SPICE is then used to investigate problems such as delay, cross-talk, reflection, or undershoot and overshoot. Junction temperature information from PCB thermal is fed into the SPICE circuit simulation for each individual IC component on a PCB or MCM.

The PARASITIC PARAMETERS product allows designers to perform two- and three-dimensional frequency-dependent capacitance, inductance, resistance, dielectric conductance, ringing, and cross-talk calculations for multiconductor and multidielectric models. This product can be applied to PCBs, VLSI, and hybrid circuit packages, connectors, multilayer wires on IC chips, resistive lines, and transmission lines.

PCB THERMAL is capable of detecting and correcting thermal problems in the design of printed circuit boards (PCB). It can analyze any type of PCB and type of component, various mounting technologies, multiple boards, as well as different cooling schemes. Temperature calculations have been verified to be within experimental accuracy. PCB SolderSim extends the thermal analysis performed by PCB THERMAL into the manufacturing area. PCB SolderSim allows the designer to analyze a variety of soldering methods such as infrared reflow, wave soldering, vapor phase reflow, and forced convection soldering. The designer can plot board and component temperatures at any time step in the soldering process. PCB SolderSim allows the designer to optimize board layout and detect problems such as cold solder joints, solder starvation, poor wetting, board warpage, and interconnect cracking.

PCB VIBRATION PLUS allows the designer to detect excessive lead and solder joint stresses due to vibration or shock stimulus. Such analysis can be critical in the design of aircraft or vehicles that are subject to sustained or random vibration. PCB FATIGUE allows the user to ensure that designs fall within the failure-free region of fatigue curves as required by the Avionics/Electronic Integrity Program of the U.S. Air Force or as needed to investigate excessive interconnect fatigue due to thermal or vibrational cyclic environments and their cumulative fatigue damage.

Interoperability. Pacific Numerix's products interface with the following CAD systems: AutoCAD-DXF, Boardmaster, Cadence, Cadnetix, Computervision, Intergraph, GDS-II Stream, Gerber Photoplot, Harris/EDA, H/P-PCDS, IGES, IBM-CBDS, Mentor Graphics, Racal Redac, P-CAD, Valid Logic, and more.

Hardware requirements. Pacific Numerix's products run on all standard UNIX-based workstations and utilize X Windows as well as MOTIF standards.

Vendor

Pacific Numerix

7333 East Doubletree Ranch Road, Suite 280

Scottsdale, AZ 85258

Tel: (602) 483-6800

Fax: (602) 483-8526

Product: Saber/InSpecs

Function. Saber/InSpecs allows users to simulate mechatronic systems. These simulations simulate the voltage and current inputs and outputs by electronic devices, as well as the mechanical load, friction, inertia, etc., of the devices that are being driven by the electronics.

Successful simulations have been carried out on floppy disk drives and electrohydraulic brake systems. These simulations enable the design team to make cross-functional trade-offs between the mechanical and electrical designs.

InSpecs includes a sensitivity analysis module which automatically varies design parameters such as shaft inertia or supply voltage value to determine which design parameters influence the product performance the most. The simulator varies the selected design parameter, runs simulations, and then tabulates the sensitivity of that particular design parameter. Multiple design parameters can then be ranked to determine which parameter will yield the best increase in system performance.

The user of the system is then left with the task of determining what the cost impact of making each of the design changes suggested by the sensitivity analysis is to the life cycle costs of the product. It is only with this life cycle cost analysis that the "best" design parameter to alter can actually be assessed.

InSpecs also provides a stress analysis. This stress analysis, though it does not perform actual finite element modeling of the mechanical elements, does allow the designer to compute the maximum stress placed on both the mechanical and electrical components of the product at various points in time. The stress analysis allows the designer to analyze startup, normal operation, and operating limit conditions to determine the appropriate requirements for each element of the design.

Saber comes with a full library of mechanical and electronic models. These models define the functionality of the mechanical or electrical device as viewed from the outside world. These boxes come in a variety of levels of detail.

Saber also supports an iterative design approach. An initial block design can be carried out and simulated. Then as each piece of the design is refined the refinement can be used in place of the initial design block for a more complete simulation. When the building blocks of the simulation incorporate both the mechanical and electronic aspects of the design, the designer can make trade-offs between these two disciplines.

Saber also allows the designer to simulate manufacturing tolerances in the electrical and mechanical parts used in the product design. Using a Monte Carlo simulation, the user can determine whether the product will function properly given the range of piece part tolerances that are used to build the product itself.

Interoperability. Saber/InSpecs can interoperate with a mechanical simulation in a variety of ways. A designer can explicitly write the equations of motion and put them in an analytic form. The designer can then implement these equations with MAST® Hardware Description Language.

Similarly a simple model can be developed in the schematic of the mechanical parts. Schematics can be used to model one-dimensional mechanical objects such as friction, spring, or damping.

Hardware requirements. Sun SPARCStation, DECstation, NEC EWS 4800, IBM RS6000, HP 300, 400, and 700 series.

Vendor

Analogy

9205 SW Gemini Drive

Beaverton, OR 97005-7156

Tel: (503) 626-9700

Fax: (503) 643-3361

Product: Working Model®

Function. Working Model is a tool for engineering analysis, animation, and prototyping. It allows an engineer to do quick kinematic analysis of rigid bodies and constraints. The rigid bodies can be designed with Working Model or imported as DXF files. The rigid bodies are predefined as either springs, actuators, motors, or joints, to name a few.

The kinematic analysis takes into account the characteristics of the environment such as air friction and gravity, as well as the properties of mass, inertia, and friction that are inherent in each individual rigid body.

Given the parameters of the environment and each rigid body, Working Model allows the user to run a simulation of the event. The user can define initial conditions, such as motor rpm or velocity, and then run the simulation to track momentum or motor torque required to maintain a constant velocity. Therefore, very accurate motor sizing can be accomplished at an early stage in the mechanical design process.

More sophisticated parameters, such as the sequencing of motors, can be controlled by interfacing Working Model to external software such as Microsoft Excel or MATLAB®.* Feedback can be incorporated by tying the equations of motion developed in Working Model to the simulation functions. For example, the designer can create a limit switch object. During the simulation the normal force of this object could be checked to determine at which frame it started to develop a force. This force could be used to simulate the closing of a contact switch, which in turn could be used in the equations of the simulation

*MATLAB is a registered trademark of The Math Works, Incorporated.

to turn off a motor or whatever. When the limit switch is triggered, this could signal an event in the overall simulation function which might, for example, stop a motor or actuator.

Interoperability. Through Dynamic Data Exchange (DDE), Working Model can interface to external software packages used to develop sophisticated control schemes of the mechanical model. Interfaces to CAD packages through .DXF files also allow users to readily import and export CAD information developed through AutoCAD and other MCAD products.

Hardware requirements. Windows: 486 microprocessor running Windows 3.1 or greater. 8 Mbits RAM and 8 Mbits of hard disk. Floating-point math coprocessor recommended. 68020-based computer or higher (Mac II or above) is required. 8 Mbits RAM and 8 Mbits of hard disk. Floating-point math coprocessor is highly recommended.

Vendor

Knowledge Revolution
66 Bovet Rd., Ste. 200
San Mateo, CA 94402
Tel: (415) 574-7777
Fax: (415) 574-7541

Electronic
Product: CAD Expert

Function. The CAD Expert series of products allows PCB designers to make both electrical and mechanical design trade-offs when designing PCBs. The CAD Expert series of tools allows the user to perform layout and autoroute tasks for designs using PCB, hybrid, HDI, and MCM design methodologies. The autorouter will take into account user-defined design parameters that reflect the manufacturing issues.

Physical Domain Simulation (PDS) allows the engineer to judge the effects caused by the physical interconnects on the performance of the board by performing signal simulation using the exact layout design. Results from the PDS can be compared to those achieved during the simulation of the hierarchical logic design.

Thermal analysis can be performed on a PCB with a range of integrated thermal analysis solutions. The thermal analysis can be performed in real time, allowing the designer to optimize board layout based on thermal characteristics. Multiple PCBs can be analyzed with a 3D system thermal analysis package based on FloTHERM™, from Flomerics Ltd.

All individual design tools are integrated with the VISUAL EDA's VISION tool framework. This framework allows individual applications to communicate in real time through a communications server, called ViewTool.

Finally CAD Expert can output NC Drill instructions to drive the manufacturing process of a PCB.

Interoperability. The VISION tool framework helps to ensure that the end user feels one consistent interface between all the diverse applications used in PCB design. This features is especially nice as the design area moves into more mechanical modeling such as thermal analysis.

Visual also interfaces to the Viewlogic schematic capture tool, as well as other PCB layout tools from PADS, P-CAD, Cadence, and Mentor.

There is a lack of interfaces to the mechanical world. Because thermal analysis is done in-house, there is little or no support for exporting or importing PCB design information into the mechanical world for incorporation into the system-level design of a product.

Hardware requirements. Sun SPARCStation, DECstation, NEC EWS 4800, IBM RS6000, HP 300, 400, and 700 series with 64 Mbits of memory, 300 Mbits of disk space (includes software project area and swap space).

Vendor

Zuken-Redac

2041 Mission College Boulevard, Suite 260

Santa Clara, CA 95054

Tel: (408) 562-0177

Fax: (408) 562-0165

Product: DF/Assembly™, DF/Thermax™

Function. Cadence Design Systems offers a full range of PCB, MMC, ASIC, and FPGA design tools that support both analog and digital designs. In addition to the traditional schematic capture, board, and chip design tools available from EDA companies, Cadence offer DF/Assembly to analyze the assembly problems inherent in the physical implementation of a circuit and DF/Thermax to address the ever-increasing heat problems found in current board designs. Both of these tools address the electromechanical concerns of the mechatronic designer.

DF/Assembly can perform numerous tasks that check the physical implementation of a PCB to ensure that it can be manufactured reliably and at minimum cost. Some of the standard checks that can be performed are checks to ensure that components are placed on the proper side of the board, component orientation constraints to minimize the number of inserter head rotations, and the analysis of process tolerances to guarantee that misregistrations will still guarantee sufficient contact to ensure signal integrity. The user can also add customize design rules. These design rules are created and modified on an easy-to-use forms-based interface.

DF/Thermax provides a set of thermal analysis tools to model such problems as heat conduction, radiation, free convection, and forced convection, as well as all conventional cooling methods such as heat sinks or fans. Users of DF/Thermax can also model multiple material layers within a MMC or IC, and multiple PCBs with components mounted on either side. Each PCB can have different and independent boundary definitions.

Interoperability. Allegro family of products including DF/Assembly and DF/Thermax interface with a variety of 3D mechanical design and analysis packages to check for interference with the housing and to perform stress, vibration, and shock analysis. Specific packages supported include Parametric Technology, Computervision, SDRC, and AutoCAD systems.

Hardware requirements. Allegro, DF/Assembly, and DF/Thermax run on Sun SPARCstation, HP9000/700, IBM RS6000, and DECstation.

Vendor

Cadence Design Systems, Inc.

555 River Oaks Parkway

San Jose, CA 95134

Tel: (408) 943-1234

Fax: (408) 943-0413

Product: EDAnavigator

Function. EDAnavigator in conjunction with the Advisor Backplane™ allows the user to explore "what-if" explorations that let the user optimize printed circuit board and module designs, as shown in Fig. B.3. The unique feature about this CAE tool is that it allows the user to explore electrical, mechanical, and manufacturing decisions concur-

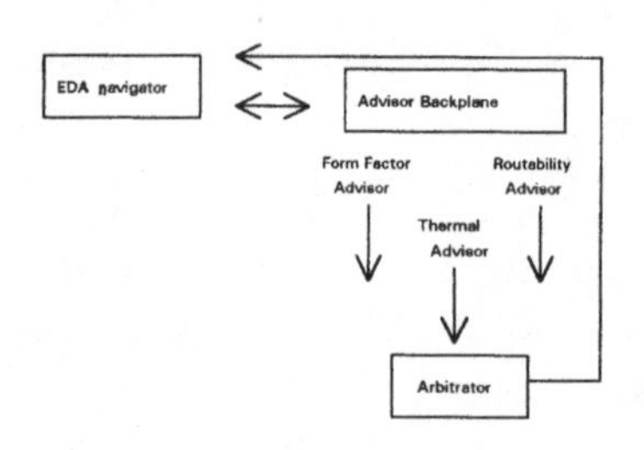

Figure B.3 EDAnavigator and Advisor Backplane.

rently. The Arbitrator™ module will listen to the design suggestions made by each of the specific design advisers. In this way a packaging decision can be weighted against its thermal impact to optimize overall board design.

The generic design of the Advisor Backplane and Arbitrator allows third-party advisers to be easily integrated into the EDAnavigator system to provide analysis for many other disciplines.

The EDAnavigator complements Harris EDA's rich offerings of SCICARDS®, for PCB design and manufacturing, and FINESSE MCM™ for multichip module designs.

Interoperability. All Harris EDA software products are tightly integrated within CAD Framework Initiative (CFI) compliant frameworks, accepting data from industry-recognized logic design software, operating within EDA frameworks, and sharing data with many leading analysis tools.

Hardware requirements. UNIX and X-windows environments on standard workstations from Sun Microsystems, Hewlett-Packard, and Digital Equipment Corporation.

Vendor

Harris EDA

7796 Victor-Mendon Rd.

Fishers, NY 14453

Tel: (716) 924-9303

Fax: (716) 924-4729

Product: Falcon Framework, BoardStation and other Mentor products

Function. Mentor, as one of the largest EDA vendors, has one of the richest sets of tools that can assist mechanical and electrical engineers to collaborate in their work. These tools range from IGES PCB to MCAD tools, to system-level design tools that can model mechanical and electrical parts of a product before the decision to partition the product into specific mechanical or electronic implementations has been made. A few of these tools are highlighted below.

The user interface glue that holds together a variety of products developed by both Mentor and third-party vendors is called the Falcon Framework®. The interface itself is based on the OSF/Motif™ standard. Through this interface end users are shielded from the complexities of heterogeneous tools and network environments. For example, an MCAD package such as HP ME10 is integrated into the framework such that the user can design a board outline in the mechanical data model, output an IGES file, and input this IGES file into BoardStation 500 without having to drop back to a Unix window to start and stop each application individually.

System Design allows designers to simulate a product before any sheet metal is stamped or any ICs have been ordered. The end user can build a "test bench" based on user interactions to simulate the product. The simulation itself can cause motors to turn on and off, switches to trigger, and control algorithms to automatically take input from the user or events in the simulation. The results of the simulation can then lead to the further refinement in design of each of the components in the simulation. Each component in the simulation can lead to software, hardware, or mechanical implementations.

Specifically tailored to mechatronic design, a suite of products has been developed to facilitate PCB data exchange between the mechanical and electrical design realms. The first tools are PCB IGES and PCB IGES+. These tools allow 2D PCB drawing information to be transferred bidirectionally to mechanical systems. The PCB mechanical Interfaces allows 3D mechanical data to be exchanged with many mechanical CAE systems. This allows PCB topology such as board shape, component shape, and component locations to be analyzed for mechanical constraints by an MCAD system. Finally a specific interface called MIBS exists between BoardStation and Hewlett-Packard's ME10 mechanical Design system. This bidirectional interface allows 2D board outlines, reference designators, mounting holes, keepouts, and other information to be transferred between the two systems.

A pair of products helps cross the electromechanical boundary of wire and cable design. Logical Cable is a schematic capture tool for wire and cable designs. With this tool the user can model connectors, components, and the cables and wires that interconnect them. Simulations can be done of these wires and the components that are connected. The wire and cable information can be used to front end several third-party MCAD systems as well as Mentor's Physical Cable. The Physical Cable product allows the user to create 3D pathways in a 3D wireframe model of the product and assign wires and cables to the pathways. Bundle diameters and wire lengths are calculated automatically. Any logic changes are reflected automatically in the physical design. A manufacturing mode generates bill of materials and formboard assembly drawings.

Interoperability. Mentor products, as with other products in the EDA industry, tend to be highly interoperable. Mentor in particular has done an excellent job of this in several areas.

The Falcon Framework provides a common user interface into which third-party packages can be seamlessly integrated for the end user. Integration doesn't stop at the user interface. Mentor provides several tools that allow applications to communicate.

APIs which conform to CFI standards enable third-party applications to communicate directly with Mentor's products. A common simulation backplane allows a variety of simulators, each written by different vendors, to run concurrently. The OpenDoor™ Partner Integrationware provides additional tools to assist vendors to integrate their applications with Mentor's products. Well over 280 vendors have integrated their products through the OpenDoor program.

Hardware requirements. DEC 3000 AXP running OSF/1, HP Series 700 running HP-UX and Series 400 Running Domain OS, IBM RS/6000 running AIX, NEC EWS4800 running EWS-UX, SPARCstations and SPARCservers running Solaris 1.x/2.x. Mentor products also support Xterminals and PC Xservers.

Vendor

Mentor Graphics

8005 SW Boeckman Rd.

Wilsonville, OR 97070-7777

Tel: (800) 547-3000

Glossary

Acceptance Test A method for evaluating a proposed system or solution based on specified criteria such as performance, capabilities, and conformity to the stated criterion. Results of evaluation generally result in "acceptance" or "not accepted," upon which payment is contingent.

Analog As it pertains to an electronic or computer system, it defines the ability to represent a state or data of continuously varying quantities such as an ammeter, power supply, etc.

ANSI Abbreviation for American National Standards Institute. It is an association formed by the U.S. government and industry to produce and disseminate drafting and manufacturing standards that are used by many companies as a foundation for communication.

Assembly Drawing A pictorial representation which defines the assembly sequence of components and subassemblies and systems. Further, it represents the major subdivisions of a product. It can be produced manually or via a CAD system.

Assessment Determining the present state of an operation, organization, department, and specific process or processes. Sometimes referred to as the As Is state.

Associativity As it pertains to computer software, it is logical linking of data or information, such as geometric entities (parts, components, subassemblies) such that with one command all information about the specified entity can be retrieved. Additionally, since all the data are related, they can be automatically updated.

Benchmarking A method of comparing an organization's specific process to the same process of other organizations, such as shipping process, order-taking process, or manufacturing process. It is used to highlight weaknesses and opportunities for improvement. It is generally advised to consider comparison to companies outside the organization's main industries.

BOM An abbreviation for bills of material. It is a list of parts, components, and subassemblies that comprise a product and the quantities needed to manufacture the product. The information is generally represented in a textual document which can be generated manually and automatically with the use of a CAD system.

Cable A combination of conductors (wires) insulated from one another. Each conductor can carry an electrical signal. The grouping of conductors has a common outer cover.

Cabling Diagram A drawing that represents the connections and physical location of the multiple conductors of a cable. It can be generated manually or via a CAD system.

CAD/CAM The abbreviation for computer-aided design/computer aided manufacturing. It refers to the integration of computers to assist the entire design-to-fabrication process.

CAE The abbreviation of computer-aided engineering. It refers to the capability to check and analyze a design to optimize the design based on a variety of conditions, such as performance requirements under high temperature, manufacturability, reaction to stress and vibration applied to the component or product. CAE can also be used to define moments of inertia, center of gravity, weight, and volume. It is performed early in the development cycle to optimize the product under multiple criteria.

CIM The abbreviation for computer integrated manufacturing. The concept of a factory or manufacturing process that is entirely automated based on consistently shared data that originated in the development or design process. These data are used by all personnel associated with the production process including planners, manufacturing engineers, schedulers, and production supervisors.

Client-server A term to describe a computer network environment where clients are computers with significant local software capabilities connected to larger computers (server) which have more computation capabilities, manage the network traffic of many clients and other servers, direct printers and peripheral devices, and have mass storage capabilities for the entire network.

CNC The abbreviation for computer numerical control. It refers to the method in which machine tools are controlled via computer instructions stored on a processor attached to the machine tool. The instructions were originally generated from a CAD/CAM system.

Compatibility The ability of a particular software program or hardware to work with other software and hardware without modification or interaction by the user. Backward compatible relates to the ability of the present or new hardware or software to work with other components of the system of previous versions. Upward compatible denotes the ability of the hardware or software to interface with new hardware or software.

Component It is at the lowest level of the product hierarchy. A collection of components is a subassembly, a collection of subassemblies constitutes an assembly, and a collection of assemblies is a product.

Concept Stage As it refers to the product life cycle and specifically to the development portion of the life cycle, it is the stage at which the product definition just begins to take shape. It is a broad definition of the product and the requirements it will address. Sometimes referred to as the "back of the napkin approach."

Configuration The combination of components, subassemblies, and assemblies that comprise a product. This includes the part numbers of the contents, the revision levels of the part numbers, and when the product is shipped the serial numbers of the assemblies and systems.

Configuration Maintenance It refers to the ability to update the product configuration after the product has been shipped when any service is performed on the product. The service may include changing assemblies or service to an assembly to fix a fault condition. These activities alter the configuration of the product, and the product configuration record needs to be modified to reflect the changes.

Configuration Management Refers to the ability to update the configuration of a product during the development and manufacturing cycle.

Corrective Maintenance After a fault has been determined, the service performed to return the product to the state of original performance.

Corrective Maintenance Time The duration required to return the product to the original performance. The time can include technical delays and logistic delays inherent in the corrective maintenance process.

Database A collection of interrelated information stored on some kind of computer medium such as magnetic tape drives or optical storage systems.

Database Management System The capability to organize and control access to information in the database. Standard capabilities are available to enter, retrieve, and update data in the system. There also is the capability to prevent duplication and unauthorized access to information.

Data Link The communication medium, controls, and interfaces which enable the transmission of data between two or more computer systems. The medium can include modems, satellites, telephone lines, fiber optic cable, digital cellular, etc.

Design Review A series of technical evaluations by a defined team with predefined acceptance criteria to ensure the product performs as designed and meets quality, reliability, manufacturability, serviceability, and cost goals.

Detailed Design Stage The stage during the development cycle, which is part of the product life cycle, when the design is formalized. Specific components and assemblies are identified and analyzed. The design is nearing final definition to be released to pilot production.

Development Cost The expenses associated with creating a product from concept definition through pilot production. It includes all personnel, equipment, prototyping materials, etc., expenses.

Development Time The duration associated with creating a product from concept definition through pilot production. It does not include the time to install full-scale production capabilities.

DFMA The abbreviation for design for manufacturability and assembly. It involves considering manufacturability and assembly constraints early in the development cycle to minimize problems during manufacturing and assembly of components.

DFR This is an abbreviation for design for reliability. During the development cycle, reliability must be designed into the product via use of highly reliable methods, the evaluation of alternative components and assemblies, and the selection of the most cost-effective reliable components and assemblies.

DFS The abbreviation for design for serviceability. A set of guidelines that focus on making the product as serviceable as possible after shipment to the customer. These guidelines need to be considered in the development cycle as early as possible so that alternatives can be evaluated as inexpensively as possible considering all the constraints.

DFT This is an abbreviation for design for testability. It is a set of guidelines which define the test methodology and testing required to meet the performance specification in the most cost-effective manner. These constraints need to be considered early in the development cycle.

DF"X" This is an abbreviation for design for anything or the design for the abilities. It refers to a set of guidelines for manufacturability, assembly, reliability, serviceability, testability which define a list of constraints that need to be considered early in the development process to optimize the product and minimize product life cycle cost.

Digital Referring to an electronic or computer system, denotes the capability to represent data in the form of digits or discrete states (i.e., 0/1 for on/off).

Distributed Processing As related to a computer system, it is the ability to have the computer software perform functions on one or more local computers, rather than one central computer processing function for a group of users.

DMU This is an abbreviation for digital mock-up. Electronic mock-up and electronic buck are equivalent terms. It is the ability to graphically represent a product, and the components and assemblies that comprise it, in a three-dimensional graphical form on a computer screen.

Documentation All handbooks, user manuals, service reference manuals, and technical descriptions that enables the effective use of a component, assembly, or product.

Drawing A pictorial representation, including dimensions necessary to fabricate and assemble, of a component, assembly, or product. Used as a method to communicate documents between customer and supplier and between functional areas.

Electrical As it refers to a component type, it is a part or assembly that provides the capability to carry current. It can also provide the logical functionality.

Electromagnetic A device such as a motor consisting of a ferromagnetic core and a coil that produces appreciable magnetic effects only when an electric current is present in the coil.

Electromagnetic Compatibility Sometimes referred to as EMC. It is a measure of tolerance of equipment or components to external magnetic fields.

Electromagnetic Interference Abbreviated EMI. It is a measure of the effect on equipment or components by electromagnetic sources, such as motors.

Fault A state of an entity, such as a component, assembly, or product, characterized by the inability to perform its specified function.

FEA The abbreviation for finite element analysis. A method to determine structural integrity of a mechanical part or assembly using mathematical equations. Can be performed manually or in an automated fashion. See CAE.

FEM The abbreviation for finite element modeling. The creation of a mathematical model to represent a part or assembly for input into a FEA program. The model is built by subdividing the design model into smaller and simpler interconnected areas or volumes, such as rectangles, triangles, bricks, or wedges.

File A collection of related information resident on a computer system which is accessed by a unique name.

File Protection A method to prevent access by unauthorized personnel or the accidental erasure of data within a file resident on the computer system.

FMEA An abbreviation for failure modes and effects analysis. It refers to a qualitative method of system analysis which involves identifying the effect by which a failure is observed. Failures exist in every component of the system, and the goal is to identify them and determine the causes and effects of each failure.

Framework A software infrastructure that enables a common operating environment for different software.

FTA The abbreviation for fault tree analysis. The logical and systematic examination of entity, such as a component or assembly, to determine and analyze the causes and consequences of potential failures.

Functional Block Diagram A high-level diagram defining a system or product where the principal parts are represented by blocks to show base functions and the relationships between the functions.

Geometric Model Constructing a three-dimensional mathematical or analytical representation of a physical object for the purposes of determining fit, response to external constraints, and for visualization.

Hardware The physical components, modules, and peripherals, such as disk drives, central processing unit, CRT terminals, and plotters, which comprise a system.

Hierarchy A graphical representation of a system or product where components and assemblies are broken down into levels of subordination. The highest level is the component or system and at the lowest level are all the components.

Interface A link which enables two different entities or systems to share information. It is the first level of integration.

Interference Checking As it relates to CAD/CAM capabilities, it is an algorithm that enables engineers to automatically examine a three-dimensional model identifying areas of fit problems between individual models of components and assemblies.

Kinematic Analysis A computer-aided process for representing the motion of parts or assemblies of a machine or system. The software allows the motion of mechanisms to be studied for interference and acceleration and to determine forces.

LAN The abbreviation for local area network. It is a combination of interconnected computer systems supported by one or more servers, usually located in one building or several interconnected buildings. Many times one building may have multiple local area networks to support different departments.

Layout A visual representation of physical components that comprise the system or product. The representation defines the components, details the interrelation of components, and identifies the arrangement of the components.

Logic Design A method to specify the functions and the interrelationship of the various parts of an electrical or electronic system.

Maintenance The collection of all activities, such as technical, administrative, and supervisory actions, with the intended purpose of retaining or restoring a system to a state where it can perform the specified functions.

Maintenance Time The duration in which a maintenance activity is performed either manually or automatically. The duration includes any delays as well as the duration to perform the actual maintenance activity.

Mechanical As it refers to a component type, it is a part or assembly that provides structure, motions, or enclosure capabilities to protect the product from exterior elements such as shock, vibration, and contamination from liquid or gaseous materials.

Mechatronics It is the preplanned activity to consider electrical, mechanical, and software constraints over the product life cycle in a simultaneous manner early in the development process.

Network An arrangement of multiple computer systems which are interconnected to enable the systems to share information via direct communication.

Optimization A systematic process whereby the best design is determined based on a set of criteria, such as fuel efficiency, cost of production, and ease of maintenance.

Parametric Model Referring to preparing geometric models, it is a method where the dimensions of the model are variables which can be modified to easily alter the model.

Physical Design The detail of the product size, shape, and structure to house other assemblies and components. There can be multiple levels of physical design such as subassembly, assembly, and product.

Physical Mock-up An actual-sized, or scaled model, of the product or system constructed to gather additional component or assembly information such as location, orientation, and fit. The objective of the mock-up or prototype is to help design or perfect the final product or process.

Pilot Production The stage of development prior to full-scale production where products are manufactured on a small scale to confirm the defined production process.

Preventive Maintenance Maintenance performed at predetermined intervals or according to prescribed criteria. It is intended to decrease the probability of failure or degradation of the entity's functionality.

Preventive Maintenance Time The duration that maintenance, of a preventive nature, is performed on an entity, including delays due to technical and logistical problems.

Printed Circuit Board A baseboard made of insulated materials and an interconnected etched copper circuit pattern on which are mounted electronic components. Also referred to as printed wiring board.

Process Map A pictorial representation of the operations required, and departments that perform the operations, of a specific procedure. The flow of the operations defines a sequence between the respective departments or functional areas.

Process Sheet A document which describes the steps necessary to accomplish a defined procedure such as an assembly of two or more components.

Product Life Cycle The duration from the time a product is conceived until retirement of a product. It includes the stages such as concept definition, manufacturing, after the sale support, and retirement.

Product Life Cycle Cost The combined expenses associated with the stages through which a product migrates including development, manufacturing, and support after the sale, or maintenance from the time the product is conceived until it is retired or discontinued.

Product Retirement A stage of the product life cycle where the product is discontinued as a planned event.

QFD The abbreviation for quality function deployment. Also referred to as house of quality. It is an analytical approach to defining and prioritizing customer needs and functionality which is being considered as part of the product package.

Scheduled Maintenance Preventive maintenance which is performed in a predetermined time frame.

Schematic A diagram of the logical arrangement of electrical and electronic components to define circuit combinations.

Server Dedicated or shared device that supports computer systems to share access to printing, plotting, mass storage of data, and to manage network communication.

Service See Maintenance.

Serviceability Performance The ability of service to be obtained within specified time and constraints, when requested by the user.

Simulation Referring to the computer-aided environment, it is an analytical process that predicts the effect of a variety of conditions and constraints, such as structural, vibration, motion, heat transfer, and electrical properties of a circuit.

Software A combination of well-defined procedures, rules, and programs based on mathematical formulas or procedures for solving predefined problems.

Solid Model A type of 3D modeling in which the solid characteristics of an object are represented in a database so that complex structures can be realistically represented.

Stress Analysis A method to determine the performance of a defined system under set conditions or constraints.

Subassembly A collection of components which when put together form a defined entity.

Support Stage Referring to the product life cycle, it is the stage after the product has been received by the customer when service may be required. The support stage ends when the customer discontinues use (retires), discards, or transfers the product to another party.

System Design The method of looking at the entire product from a top-down approach considering the relationship of all entities including components and subassemblies.

Useful Life The duration beginning when the product is put into use and ending when the product is removed from use owing to obsolescence or when the failure intensity becomes unacceptable or when the product is considered unrepairable as a result of a fault.

WAN The abbreviation for wide area network. It is a collection of computer systems spread through many countries, states, and cities that are interconnected to share information.

Workstation A computer system which can perform certain functions, independent of another computer, on the processor located in the computer system.

Additional Reading

Albus, J: *Japanese Technology Assessment,* 1986.
Boothroyd and Dewhurst: *Design for Assembly: A Designer's Handbook,* 1983.
Carver, G. P.: "Concurrent Engineering through Product Data Standards," *NTIS,* 1991.
Carver, G. P.: "Multi-Enterprise Concurrent Engineering through International Standards," *NTIS,* 1991.
Fong, Jeffrey: "Integration of Analysis and Data Bases for Engineering Decision Making," *Computers in Mechanical Engineering,* July 1988.
Fulton, Robert: "A Framework for Innovation," *Computers in Mechanical Engineering,* March 1987.
Goffin, Keith: Gaining a Competitive Advantage from Support, *AFSM International,* April 1994.
Harp, Jim: "Back to Basics," *Manufacturing Engineering,* October 1985.
Hewitt, J. R.: "Mechatronics—Are We Ready?" Loughborough University of Technology.
Jones, Bark Meyer, and Davis: "Issues in the Design and Implementation of a System Architecture of CIM," *International Journal of Computer Integrated Manufacturing,* vol. 2, no. 2, 1989.
Jurstein, William: "CAD/CAM Systems," *Manufacturing Management,* February 1984.
Mills, Robert: "Linking CAD & CAM," *CAE,* September 1987.
Nevins and Whitney (eds.): *Concurrent Design of Products and Processes: A Strategy for the Next Generation of Manufacturing,* McGraw-Hill, New York, 1989.
Preston, Mike: "What Is Mechatronics?" Loughborough University of Technology.
Reisdorf, William: "Extending DBMS's for Engineering Applications," *Computers in Mechanical Engineering,* March 1987.
Tomkinson, Donald: "Role of CAD/CAM Suppliers in Facilitating Mechatronics," *Electro 92 Conference Proceedings,* May 1992.
Tomkinson, Donald: "Mechatronics: Getting MEs and EEs to Work in Harmony," *Machine Design,* January 1992.
Tomkinson, Donald: "Mechatronics: A New Flavor in Integration," *Automation,* December 1991.
Villemeur, Allain: *Reliability, Availability, Maintainability and Safety Assessment,* vol. 1, Wiley, New York, 1992.
Villemeur, Allain: "Application of CE to Mechanical Systems Design," CALS Industry Steering Group, *Technical Report* 002, June 16, 1989, 97 pp.
Villemeur, Allain: "Improving Engineering Design: Designing for Competitive Advantage," Committee on Engineering Design Theory and Methodology; Manufacturing Studies Board, Commission on Engineering and Technical Systems, National Research Council, 1991.
Villemeur, Allain: "Thinking Mechatronically," *Managing Automation,* February 1988.
Wakely and Sharp: "Vehicle Wiring Harness Design at Land Rover," CV European Users' Group Conference Papers, *Prime Computer,* April 1989.
Yankee Group: *CIM: Toward 1992.*

Bibliography

"A Case Study in Change at Harvard," *Business Week,* Nov. 15, 1993.
Angelucci, George, "Cycle-Time Reduction: A Minute Saved is a Minute Earned," AFSM International, April 1994, p. 29.
Atkinson and Glasscook, "An Implementation of a Product Data Management System," *Proceedings of the ASME International Computers in Engineering,* Aug. 1990, p. 37.
Boes, Bruce, "Implementing Mechatronics: A Design Approach for Optimum Product Development," *ECN,* 1993.
Boothroyd, Geoffery, "Estimate Costs at an Early Stage," *American Machinist,* Penton Publishing, Cleveland, OH, Aug. 1988.
Clausing, Don, *Total Quality Development: A Step-by-Step Guide to World Class Concurrent Engineering,* ASME Press, New York, 1994.
Clausing, Don, "Concurrent Engineering Design and Productivity," International Conference, Honolulu, Feb. 1991.
Comerford, Richard Sr., Editor, "Meca...what?," *IEEE Spectrum,* Aug. 1994.
"Coming Off the Drawing Board: Better Engineers?" *Business Week,* Aug. 1993.
Computervision, "From Wood and Canvas to World Class," *Contact,* Summer 1992, p. 5.
Computervision, "Simultaneous Engineering as a Competitive Advantage," *Computer Aided Engineering,* Oct. 1990, p. C3.
Constance, Joseph, "DFMA: Learning to Design for Manufacture and Assembly," *Mechanical Engineering,* May 1992, p. 70.
Dahir, Mubarak, "Educating Engineers for the Real World," *Technology Review,* Aug./Sept. 1993.
"Defining Intel: 25 Years/25 Events," Intel Corporation, Santa Clara, CA, 1993.
Durfee, William, "Engineering Education Gets Real," *Technology Review,* MIT Association of Alumni and Alumnae, Feb./March 1994.
Flint, Jerry, "Empowered," *Forbes,* Feb. 15, 1993.
Gottschalk, Mark A., "How Boeing Got to 777th Heaven," *Design News,* Sept. 12, 1994, p. 50.
Hamel and Prahalad, "Competing for the Future," *Harvard Business Review,* July–Aug. 1994, p. 122.
Hars, Adele, "Global Standards Change the Face of Product Design," *Design News,* Sept. 26, 1994, p. 23.
"History of Yaskawa," Yaskawa corporate records, Yaskawa Electric America, Inc., Northbrook, IL.
Iacocca, Lee, and Novak, William, *Iacocca,* Bantam Books, New York, 1984.
Katzenbach, Jon, and Smith, Douglas, *The Wisdom of Teams,* Harper Collins Publishers, New York, 1993.
King, Russell, "Chrysler's Cirrus Carves New Niche," *Design News,* Oct. 10, 1994, p. 29.
LeDuc and Hogan, "Outsourcing Changes the Engineering Lineup," *Design News,* Oct. 10, 1994, p. 128.
"Manufacturing into the late 1990's," PA Consulting Group Report for DTI.
McDonald, Robert, "The Critical Importance of Database Management in Industrial Automation," *Proceedings of the 1990 ASME International Computers in Engineering,* Aug. 5–9, 1990, p. 131.

Millbank, John, "MECHA-WHAT!," *Mechatronics Forum Newsletter,* no. 6, Summer 1993.
Morgan, M. Granger, "Accreditation and Diversity in Engineering Education," *Science,* Aug. 21, 1990.
Murray, Charles J., "Ford, DOE Collaborate on Product Data Transfer," *Design News,* Oct. 10, 1994, p. 49.
Nevens, Summe and Uttal, "Commercializing Technology: What the Best Companies Do," *Harvard Business Review,* May–June 1990, p. 158.
Peters, Thomas J., and Waterman, Robert H., *In Search of Excellence,* Warner Books Inc., New York, 1982.
Puttre, Michael, "Putting Optimization Routines in the Loop," *Mechanical Engineering,* July 1993, p. 77.
Rovetta, Alberto, "A New Technology with an Old Face and a Proud Heritage," *Mechatronics,* vol. 1, No. 2, 1991.
Schaeffer, Robert, and Thomson, Harvey, "Successful Change Programs Begin with Results," *Harvard Business Review,* Jan/Feb 1992.
Sherman, Stanford, "Are You as Good as the Best in the World," *Fortune,* Dec. 13, 1993, p. 95.
Shina, Sammy, "New Rules for World-Class Companies," *IEEE Spectrum,* July 1991, p. 24.
Souder, William E., *Managing New Product Innovations,* MacMillan Publishing Co., New York, 1986.
Teresko, John, "Service Now a Design Element," *Industry Week,* Feb. 7, 1994.
Tomkinson, Donald, "Getting MEs and EEs to Work In Harmony," *Machine Design,* Jan. 23, 1994, p. 61.
Ury, William, and Fisher, Roger, *Getting to Yes,* Penguin Books, New York, 1983.
Villemeur, Allain, *Reliability, Availability, Maintainability and Safety Assessment,* vol. 1, John Wiley & Sons, 1992, p. 112.

Index

ABOUT THE AUTHORS

DONALD TOMKINSON has been involved with mechatronic issues for more than ten years. Over that time, he has identified and implemented a diverse range of mechatronic solutions for many of the world's largest automotive, aerospace, and machinery manufacturers.

JAMES HORNE began working with mechatronics over a decade ago. His experience began with vision-guided robotic welding work cells for the automotive industry and subsequently moved to the development of harness/cabling CAD/CAM design software for automotive, aerospace, and mechanical machinery manufacturers.